Foreword

HSE is pleased to see industry preparing supporting guidance for designers. CIRIA has a reputation for preparing useful "good practice" guidance and it is noted that the existing CDM guidance for designers is being updated both as guidance for designers as they consider hazards and risks arising during construction (updating the existing guide) and during the use of a structure as a workplace (this new companion guide).

It is a requirement of CDM2007 that designers consider the hazards and risks which affect those using workplaces they have designed and also ensure compliance with the Workplace (Health, Safety and Welfare) Regulations 1992. It is hoped that designers will use this guidance to raise their awareness of the issues they have to address.

CDM2007 is designed to bring the consideration of the actual potential hazards and risks on each project to the forefront of a designer's work, and this guide should assist designers in carrying out their duties by seeking to eliminate hazards, minimising the risks which remain and communicating residual risks to others. This activity must be at the core of a designer's work whether on a small factory extension or a new transport interchange.

Health & Safety Executive

About this guide

The Construction (Design and Management) Regulations 2007 (known as "CDM2007") affect all construction work of any significance. The Regulations place duties upon all designers and this guide is designed to assist in fulfilling those duties with respect to workplaces "in use".

CDM2007 builds upon earlier health and safety legislation by imposing a framework of duties so that all the parties to a construction project must consider health and safety. The Regulations have an Approved Code of Practice L144 (known as the ACoP) titled *Construction (Design and Management) Regulations 2007*, which has legal status and must be referred to alongside CDM2007.

Guidance has been prepared by industry working groups and may be freely accessed through www.citb-constructionskills.co.uk/cdm

This guide addresses workplace "in-use" hazards and has a companion publication, CIRIA C662, *CDM2007 – Construction work sector guidance for designers,* which addresses construction hazards.

READERSHIP

This guidance has been produced for designers wishing to develop a full understanding of their function with respect to relevant workplace "in-use" hazards that need to be considered under CDM. It focuses upon the management of hazard and risk but also provides information about designers' CDM duties in general.

The word "designer" is a defined term under CDM2007 and has a broad meaning, going beyond the traditional definition, to include anyone who makes input to design decisions. This is discussed in the guidance.

Each designer will have his or her own area of decision-making, which will affect risks "in-use". Designers need to concentrate on the decisions that they can influence while being aware of the concerns of other designers, which may be affected by their actions.

A general understanding of CDM2007 and its ACoP L144 is assumed. For further information see Appendix C, Sources of further information.

In particular, when considering construction hazards, designers may refer to CIRIA publication C662: *CDM2007 – construction work-sector guidance for designers.*

KEY POINTS

It must be understood that anyone who acts as a designer as defined by CDM2007 (including a client who imposes specific requirements), has duties as a designer under CDM.

> *All those who contribute to design decisions affecting subsequent use of a structure must consider the hazards and risks involved. This requires an understanding of workplace "in-use" conditions, including related facilities, management activities and the types of accidents and health issues that need to be considered.*

This report provides a wealth of accessible information about health and safety issues in the use of a wide range of structures. The consideration of these matters must be an integral part of the design decision process. Each designer has a part to play, working as a member of the design team who must make decisions related to health and safety in a coordinated manner, led by the CDM coordinator. This report is not, however, a textbook; rather it provides prompts to make a designer think and apply his or her knowledge.

The object of CDM is to embed health and safety management into projects. All designers have a role to play and must communicate with others to provide information about health and safety for those who operate workplaces, as they plan and manage work. The dividing line between operating a building, day-to-day facilities management and maintenance activities which are construction activities under CDM, has not always been clear. Because designers now must consider all these aspects under CDM, this no longer matters.

A designer's duties under CDM require considerable common sense and openness in order to relate to the other duty-holders in a constructive manner. Duties must be carried out in a way that is proportional to the type of project and the likely level of risk.

Information prepared by designers for the purposes of CDM must:

- focus on health and safety information which competent people would not reasonably anticipate
- be specific to the project
- reflect the level of risk and complexity
- be concise.

> *Particular care is needed to prepare concise, focused documentation that is relevant to the project in hand. In this way, it will be of immediate use to the people who need to use it. To achieve this, the use of lengthy, standardised or off-the-shelf, catch-all documents must be avoided. The aim is to produce relevant information that is proportionate to the project and its risks and, hence, useful and cost-effective.*

How to use this guide

The guide has been structured so that it can be read from cover-to-cover or consulted by those who simply need to dip in for specific information. The guidance is designed to provoke thought and to improve understanding and knowledge, but it cannot provide complete information for every circumstance. As with all checklist guidance, the user must ask "is there anything else, for this particular project?"

Chapter 1 – Introduction

This introduces the requirements of CDM2007 and examines the issues which arise.

Chapter 2 – Information about the Workplace Regulations

CDM2007 is specific that the requirements of the Workplace Regulations are provided for by designers. This Chapter outlines the requirements as set out in the regulations themselves and as expanded upon in their ACoP.

Chapter 3 – Information about hazards

A range of typical hazards is examined, providing prompts to designers about the issues involved and suggesting key references where further information may be found. Space is provided for users to add their own notes and references.

Chapter 4 – Information about typical workplaces

A small selection of typical workplaces is examined, showing the types of underlying issues which need to be considered when examining "in-use" hazards.

Appendices

A hazard checklist is provided which may assist designers and an example of its use is shown. Also, further sources of information are referenced.

Acknowledgements

The Contractor for the work leading to this publication was Alan Gilbertson of Gilbertson Consultants Limited.

Project Steering Group

The preparation of this publication was guided by a Steering Group, established by CIRIA to advise on technical issues. CIRIA and Gilbertson Consultants Limited would like to express their thanks and appreciation to all members of the Project Steering Group and their organisations.
This comprised:

Paul Craddock	Arup
Matt Harrison	Arup
David Lambert	Kier Group
Andrew Stevens	Atkins
Bob Keenan	Sheppard Robson
Peter Sheaves	Consultant
David Watson	WSP
John Carpenter	Consultant.

Assistance was given with review of the references by NBS Building Regulations. Andrew East and colleagues at the Health & Safety Executive also provided valuable assistance.

Contents

1   Introduction

1.1   WHAT THE REGULATIONS REQUIRE

The Regulations state in Reg 11, with bold and underlining added by the author of this guide:

(2) *The duties in paragraphs (3) and (4) shall be performed so far as is reasonably practicable, taking account of other relevant design considerations*

(3) *Every designer shall in preparing or modifying a design which may be used in construction work in Great Britain*

avoid foreseeable risks to the health and safety of any person *–*

    (a) *carrying out construction work;*

    (b) *liable to be affected by such construction work;*

    (c) *cleaning any window or any transparent or translucent wall, ceiling or roof in or on a structure;*

    (d) *maintaining the permanent fixtures and fittings of a structure; or*

    (e) ***using a structure designed as a workplace.***

(4) *In discharging the duty in paragraph (3), the designer shall -*

    (a) ***eliminate hazards which may give rise to risks; and***

    (b) ***reduce risks from any remaining hazards,***

and in doing so shall give collective measures priority over individual measures.

(5) ***In designing any structure for use as a workplace the designer shall take account of the provisions in the Workplace (Health, Safety and Welfare) Regulations 1992 which relate to the design of, and materials used in, the structure.***

(6) *The designer shall take all reasonable steps to provide with his design sufficient information about aspects of the design of the structure or its construction or maintenance as will adequately assist*

    a) *Clients*

    b) *Other designers; and*

    c) *Contractors*

To comply with their duties under these regulations.

Paragraph (5) the Workplace (Health, Safety and Welfare) Regulations 1992 (referred to hereafter as "the Workplace Regulations") contains *specific requirements* for the provision of welfare facilities and these include:

- □   maintenance/cleaning to be done
- □   not to be over-crowded
- □   suitable work-stations
- □   organised traffic routes (people and vehicles)
- □   suitable and sufficient toilets, washing facilities, drinking water
- □   facilities to store clothes and change
- □   facilities to rest and eat meals.

Further summarised details are provided in Section 2 below. These requirements lie alongside the more general requirement in Reg 11(3) and (4) to eliminate hazards and reduce risks, so far as is reasonably practicable.

1.2   HOW THE APPROACH REQUIRED BY CDM2007 RELATES TO PREVIOUS PRACTICE

There is nothing intrinsically new about the consideration of hazard and risk in the workplace. Those responsible for workplaces have for many years been required to carry out formal risk assessments and to take action accordingly. When a new workplace is handed over to those responsible for its management, one of their first activities must be to carry out the first risk assessment of the new environment, as required by the Management of Health and Safety at Work Regulations. *All this activity is highly specific to a particular workplace and takes advantage of the detailed knowledge and control available to the managers of the workplace.*

Before CDM2007 designers normally carried out "in-use risk" assessment for a future workplace in a less formal manner, for example by relying upon complying with standards laid down by others:

- <u>authorities</u> (the Building Regulations, the Disability and Discrimination Act and specific regulations applying to particular industry workplaces)

- <u>clients</u> (such as the NHS) who set their own requirements

- <u>industry bodies</u> (such as the The British Council for Offices), who formulate standards for work sectors

- <u>technical bodies</u> (such as IEE and CIBSE), who set technical standards.

This activity has sometimes tended to be generic and may not always have responded in detail to a specific workplace situation. Often there was little formal communication on risk between designers and those taking occupation, although the Health and Safety File ("the File") – required by CDM since 1995 – should contain useful background information, particularly for work on cleaning, maintaining and adapting "structures" as defined in the regulations (ie a wide range of buildings and infrastructure), and dealing with building systems such as electricity, ventilation etc.

Under CDM2007, structure-specific workplace "in-use" hazards and risks need to be considered by designers and this guidance is designed to assist with that process. Exactly how this is done will vary greatly – depending on the situation – but it is anticipated that associated information provided by designers (normally in the O+M Manual) will provide a springboard for subsequent workplace risk assessment; indeed, in many cases those responsible will have been acting as advisers/designers during the design process. See also Section 1.6, Who are designers?

Of course, it must be recognised that frequently, designers will not have access to detailed knowledge available to the managers of the workplace and decisions will need to be made accordingly. In all cases the primary responsibility for risk assessment will remain with those able to assess and manage the residual risks. Designers will however have responsibility for the environment which they have created.

As an illustration, two examples are given below which demonstrate the importance of providing safe access into buildings, where moisture on footwear may cause slipping on a smooth surface.

Example 1:

This entrance, featured in CIRIA Publication C652, *Safer surfaces to walk on – reducing the risk of slipping*, has a small area of entrance matting which is adjacent to, and interspersed with, low slip-resistance tiling. During wet weather it can be unsafe to walk on.

Figure 1.1   *Unsafe access into a building*

Example 2:

This entrance has a large protective canopy and the walking surface within the entrance lobby is carpet. During wet weather it is safe to walk on.

Figure 1.2   *Entrance to the QE2 Conference Centre, London*

1.3   WHAT ARE WORKPLACE "IN-USE" HAZARDS FOR THE PURPOSES OF CDM?

CDM2007 does not limit the hazards to be considered although it does require that the matters specifically covered by the Workplace Regulations are taken into account. The limitation to those in a structure "designed as a workplace" arises from the remit of the Health & Saftey Ececutive (HSE), which refers specifically to the workplace. However, with the possible exception of private domestic housing it is difficult to think of a structure which is not of necessity, on occasion, a workplace and therefore designed as such. Even private domestic housing may not be excluded, as the responsibility of designers to consider risks to those carrying out future maintenance work etc has no limit under CDM (regardless of limits to other aspects of CDM). Just as a plumber working on a water-tank in a loft is necessarily then in a workplace, it could be argued that consideration of workplace "in-use" hazards and risks should apply to private housing too.

Whether such thinking applies only to the area involved or means that the CDM issues apply to the whole structure may be resolved in the courts. Designers, however, would be well-advised to design for all people to the same standard.

Workplace "in-use" hazards will necessarily involve a much wider range of hazards than those encountered in construction. However, in a similar manner the designer has to identify what they are and manage the risks in the same manner. This guide provides information to assist that process and addresses a range of hazards of both a specific and a general nature.

There are a great many generic and specific workplace hazards which present risks to our health and safety in the workplace, and they could be segmented in a variety of ways.

This guide identifies "families" of types of hazard and then addresses specific types of hazard within that family. The families are:

1. **Physical environment** (eg lighting, noise, vibration, temperature, wetness and humidity, draughts)

2. **Chemical and/or biological environment** (eg sanitary conditions, animals, moulds and fungal growths, other hazardous materials, smoke, dusts and fibres, other contamination/pollution)

3. **Hazardous systems** (eg electricity, hot water and steam, piped gases/liquids, hot surfaces, storage)

4. **Normal activities** (eg posture and manual handling, use of vehicles, use of plant and equipment, industrial processes, use of doors and windows/glazing, use of lifts escalators and moving walkways)

5. **Slips and trips** (eg whilst in motion on floors and ramps, whilst using stairs or escalators, whilst essentially static)

6. **Working at height** (eg using access equipment such as ladders, at unprotected edges and adjacent to fragile surfaces)

7. **Abnormal events** (eg fire, explosion, falling objects, disproportionate collapse, drowning and asphyxiation, crowding, malicious human intervention)

Regardless of the range of workplace in-use hazards identified and examined in this guide, designers must think through the potential hazards present in each specific situation; there may be others which are not examined here – but the process for considering them will be the same.

1.4   HOW ARE HAZARDS TO BE ASSESSED AND MANAGED BY DESIGNERS?

As explained above, there are easily-accessed sources of advice on this subject. To demonstrate how they might apply in an 'in-use' situation, the table below examines one particular hazard. The table is intended to demonstrate the thought process and does not imply that a risk assessment has to be recorded in this manner or that the outcome would always be the same. See also Appendix B for a further example of the process.

Scenario:		
At a new high-street tyre shop, operatives will be required to load scrap tyres into 2.4 m-high bins.		
Hazard identified		Working at height and manual handling while disposing of scrap tyres. Manhandling tyres of various weights (increasingly heavy for SUVs) up to a platform and throwing them into the bin presents risk of musculo-skeletal damage and losing balance etc on the steps and platform.
Key features		The risk of injury from a single operation is small but operatives do this repeatedly and, within the tyre shop group, there have been examples of reportable accidents and time off work due to falls and sprains.
"ERIC" by the designers (see note below)	**E**limination of hazard or substitution of lower-risk hazard and **R**eduction of risk	The design team investigated the feasibility of sinking bins into a pit with a safety railing around it. This would cost £10k for the pit and its railing and drainage. There would also be a cost of £5k in adapting the skip delivery lorry so that it could load and unload at the pit. A time and motion study at an existing outlet showed that time saved would recoup the costs within five years, and there would be less risk of accidents and injuries, etc causing time off work. Operatives were supportive of the idea. Removal of the hazard was therefore the preferred and selected option.
	Provision of **I**nformation	For management: Requirement for annual inspection and if necessary maintenance of safety railings and pit drain. For users: Not required.
	Control measures	The designer team suggested: Provide safe access into the pit for occasional clean-out. Provide a padlock to the access gate to prevent entry by unauthorised persons.

Figure 1.3 *Example of the consideration of a particular "in-use" hazard*

Note: The requirement for designers to eliminate hazards and reduce risks will normally involve activities in the acronym ERIC – Eliminate, Reduce, Inform, Control. Further guidance on ERIC is provided at the industry guidance website – www.citb-constructionskills.co.uk/CDM

1.5 WHO ARE AFFECTED BY "IN-USE" HAZARDS

CDM2007 refers to "any person using a structure designed as a workplace", which will include not only people who work there but others using the structure (usually a building).

Although others affected by the use of the structure (eg neighbours or passers-by) are not specifically mentioned, designers have a duty of care to them under the Health and Safety at Work Act 1974, and possibly other legislation (eg for environmental noise or chimney emissions). Many hazards which affect the users of a building may affect others (eg noise, gases, dust etc).

1.6 WHO ARE DESIGNERS?

The role of "designer" is widely cast under CDM. CDM2007 makes it clear (Reg 2(1)) that this can include a client while the ACoP (Paragraphs 115, 116) enumerates at length the sorts of people who may act as "designers" in the widest sense, by making decisions or providing details.

In considering "in-use" hazards there will be many where the party acting as client has a central role to play (be it the end-user of a project or a project promoter who will be selling-on or renting in some manner). The CDM coordinator will have to ensure that this party (called the "client" in this guide) makes appropriate inputs which are coordinated with the work of others.

In some situations, specialist inputs may be needed and the CDM coordinator will need to ensure that the appropriate steps are taken to obtain them. In certain circumstances it may also be appropriate to consult those who will work in a new or refurbished structure.

> *A developer client was constructing a factory which was to be let to a company which specialised in the zinc-coating of metal products. The special requirements of the process needed to be taken into account when selecting floor finishes and designing the air supply and extract, alarm and guarding systems. The CDM coordinator asked that the appropriate expertise be made available to the project and the client involved his future tenant for the necessary expertise.*

1.7   PROVISION OF INFORMATION

Just as for construction, the contractors will require information from the client and the designers, for the management of a workplace "in-use". Those responsible for managing and operating will require information to enable them to discharge their duties under the Management of Health and Safety at Work Regulations.

Information of this nature has traditionally been made available by the construction team in the Operation and Maintenance (O+M) Manual. The manner in which the information is provided will need to be decided and take account of:

    (a)   the needs of the client, the occupier and the operator

    (b)   who will hold the information and in what form

    (c)   how the information will be made available for reference

    (d)   arrangements for keeping the information up-to-date.

Exactly how this is done will need to agreed with the Client, before documentation starts. The CDM coordinator will be a key player in ensuring that appropriate decisions are made and carried through. Note that a multi-discipline approach will normally be necessary.

An example of the type of information which the operator will find useful is provided in Table 1.1. It is not intended to be complete as each structure will present different requirements. It may however assist in promoting thought.

Table 1.1   *Examples of information arising from workplace "in-use" issues*

Topic	Information
Flooring (for each area/type, including stairs)	Slip Resistance Value (SRV) to be maintained; maintenance regime to be followed.
Fire	Compartmentation strategy and equipment. Smoke management strategy and equipment. Escape strategy, signage and equipment. Fire-fighting strategy, information and equipment. Emergency power system and fail-safe provision.
Re-lamping	Strategy, requirements and means of access.
Window maintenance and cleaning	Strategy, requirements and means of access.
Cleaning facade	Strategy, requirements and means of access.
Cleaning roof and gutters	Strategy, requirements and means of access.
Cleaning floors, walls and ceilings	Strategy, requirements and means of access.
Cleaning work surfaces	Strategy and requirements.
Waste management	Strategy and provision.
Process information	Summary of the process and information about the hazards and risks at the design stage.
Ergonomics	Outline policy.
Circulation strategy (for vehicles and pedestrians)	Strategy and provision.
Storage and transportation strategy (for materials and products)	Strategy and provision.
Separation from hazards	Strategy and provision of controls including escape systems.
Working at height	Strategy, requirements and means of access.
Mechanical plant maintenance and replacement	Strategy, requirements and means of access.
Façade maintenance and repair	Strategy, requirements and provisions built in.
Inspection, maintenance and use of working platforms, including systems	Strategy, requirements and means of access.
Roof access for maintenance and repair	Strategy, requirements and provisions built in.
Inspection, maintenance and use of restraint and suspension systems	Strategy, requirements and means of access.
Asbestos management	Survey data, analysis results and condition records.
Confined spaces	Identify spaces and residual hazards, explain how access is (a) prevented and (b) permitted under controlled conditions, explaining the suggested precautions.
Crowds	Strategy and provision.

NOTE: A topic would only apply when it is a significant feature of the workplace.

The guidance should be used to prompt and supplement the thinking of the design team and the CDM coordinator. It should not be used blindly as a box-ticking exercise. Each workplace will be unique, and it is the responsibility of the designers and the CDM coordinator to respond to a particular situation in an appropriate manner.

One option will be for the design team to meet and – led by the CDM coordinator – to run through the hazards they identify. They could then look through this guide to see whether that prompts other hazards to be identified and – importantly – to start to assess the levels of risk and how the design will respond. This process need not normally take an excessively long time; it should be proportionate to the levels of risk which obtain.

What is important is that consideration of the hazards and risks takes place and that appropriate decisions are made and then respected by designers and documented as appropriate into the project. This has already been happening with respect to cleaning and maintenance; it has often been through team discussion that sensible risk-reduction/management measures have been agreed and put into action. See CIRIA publication C611 *Access for maintenance and repair*, for discussion of this aspect of the workplace.

Many hazards will be seen to be adequately dealt with by simply complying with other regulations and by common-sense measures. Others may be more complex and, because of the severity of the risks involved, a more advanced approach may be required. As an example, one of the most common forms of accident is slipping or tripping over. Because of this, the HSE sponsored the preparation of CIRIA Guide C652, *Safer surfaces to walk on – reducing the risk of slipping* ,which addresses the risks in detail and explains how they may be considered both at the design stage and subsequently, "in-use".

As a further example, it is increasingly understood that long-term damage to health can arise through the execution of repetitive actions which are not unduly difficult or onerous if undertaken occasionally. The construction industry has responded to this by measures such as adopting more mechanical lifting devices (eg for kerb stones) and reducing the weight of blocks to be handled and the normal weight of bags of cement and other products. Similar issues will arise in any workplace and designers should examine them during their consideration of "in-use" hazards and risks – for example by reducing the requirement for manual lifting and carrying. Workplace "in-use" issues which arise frequently include:

- ❑ selection of flooring materials which do not require high levels of grinding or buffing to maintain their performance and which maintain their properties over their design life
- ❑ sizing of lifts to avoid the need to manhandle objects upstairs
- ❑ provision of permanently fixed access equipment to avoid having to manhandle moveable access equipment and siting of the permanent equipment so that it can be easily and safely accessed for maintenance, testing and use
- ❑ avoiding ladders and trap-doors into plant-rooms and onto roofs

- provision of lifting devices for raising tools and components to and from plant and equipment including in plant-rooms
- provision of adequate working space in plant rooms and means of handling and installing replacement plant.

Similar issues will arise in most workplaces.

Material provided in this guide may be used to assist hazard identification and specific measures which need to be taken, as follows:

- **Section 2** summarises the specific requirements of the Workplace Regulations and its ACoP. While Section 2 enables designers rapidly to gain an overview of the Workplace Regulations, members of the team must between them be familiar with the requirements in detail.

- **Section 3** examines a range of hazards and provides reference to further detailed guidance; the information provided should prompt discussion and further exploration of the issues; the team (to be competent – a requirement of CDM) should include experts in all the areas relevant to the project, or additional input must be sought from appropriately experienced designers or experts

- **Section 4** looks at some typical workplaces, demonstrating the type of thinking required; again the team should have expertise in the type of workplace being designed

- **Appendices A and B** provide a checklist which may be used or adapted as a basis for recording consideration of hazards and risks, with an example

- **Appendix C** provides references of which designers need to be aware, including requirements for particular activities and industries.

It will be noted that disability is not specifically mentioned in the tables. The Building Regulations, the Workplace Regulations and the Disability Discrimination Act specifically require that these needs be considered and this must be borne in mind when considering all hazards.

> *Designers should use this guide to stimulate their consideration of hazards and risks based upon their own experience and expertise; where they are unsure, expert advice should be sought. Nothing in this guide is intended to be prescriptive or to set in place requirements which designers have to follow, beyond the requirements of CDM2007.*

2. Summary of the specific requirements of The Workplace (Health, Safety and Welfare) Regulations 1992 and its ACoP L24

In outline the Workplace Regulations apply to any workplace except:

- operational ships (covered by separate legislation)
- construction (covered by CDM2007)
- mines (covered by separate legislation).

Certain workplaces are exempt from some of the requirements:

- for any temporary worksites, Regs 20–25 apply only so far as is reasonably practicable (SFARP)
- for workplaces in/on an operational aircraft, locomotive or rolling stock, trailer or semi-trailer, only Reg 13 applies and then only if stationary inside a workplace
- for workplaces in the countryside which are remote from an undertaking's main buildings, only Regs 20–22 apply and then only SFARP
- for workplaces at a quarry or above ground at a mine, only Reg 12 applies and then only for a floor or traffic route inside a building.

Generally the requirements are absolute. Even where there is an exemption from this, the general risk management requirements of CDM2007 will still apply. The requirements are very specific and (like the Building Regulations), designers need to be familiar with the requirements which impinge upon their areas of expertise; CDM coordinators need to be familiar with them all to enable them to manage interfaces between designers. The Workplace Regulations suggest that reference is made to local authorities and fire departments, as well as to the wealth of guidance published by the HSE.

For the purposes of this guide, a summary of the requirements expressed in the Workplace Regulations and the associated ACoP L24 is given in the following table (Table 2.1 Summary of the Workplace Regulations). The information provided paraphrases the requirements to give an easily-accessed view of what the Regulations and ACoP cover. It can be seen that the requirements reflect the standard of provision which is expected in today's society where everyone's needs should be respected and met in a sensible manner. They align with the Building Regulations, albeit with some additional requirements and advice reflecting workplace requirements. They are directed towards people at work. In many workplaces there will be others present for a variety of reasons (students, patients, visitors etc as well as passers-by), and their requirements will also need to be met in a sensible manner. Similarly, although disabled persons are specifically mentioned in some places, design in its generality must take account of the needs of disabled people.

Table 2.1 *Summary of the Workplace Regulations*

Reg	Summary of requirements	Notes
1–4		These are opening sections and do not contain specific technical requirements.
5	**MAINTENANCE** A workplace and its equipment and systems must be properly *cleaned and maintained.*	Designers need to consider how the cleaning and maintenance of the structure (including its systems), can be done with minimum risk and what information needs to be provided, what needs to be done, and how to do it safely.
6	**VENTILATION** An enclosed workplace must be adequately *ventilated* with fresh (uncontaminated) air without excessive drafts, smells or humidity and without risk of Legionnaire's disease.	There is a requirement for alarms where necessary for H&S reasons. There are some exceptions to the requirement for ventilation, where the work is in a "confined space" and special measures are taken such as the provision of breathing apparatus, although such spaces, or the need for personnel to enter them, should be designed out wherever reasonably practicable.
7	**TEMPERATURE** A workplace must be reasonably *warm*, without problems from escaping vapours emanating from the heating system, and with thermometers to keep a check.	Provision of thermometers will normally be part of the fit-out.
8	**LIGHTING** A workplace must be **adequately lit, with natural lighting SFARP,** and with suitably **emergency lighting** where loss of lighting would present a risk.	*Provision of work-spaces without good natural lighting should normally be avoided.* Provision of emergency lighting beyond what is required for safe egress in a fire will be dictated by the work processes.
9	**CLEANLINESS AND WASTE** The *structure and its contents need to be kept clean and waste dealt with.*	Designers need to consider *how the surfaces of the structure can be cleaned with minimum risk. Information on what needs to be done and how to do it safely should be provided.* Designers also need to consider *how waste will be managed in a safe manner. Information on the waste management strategy and what needs to be done should be provided.*
10	**ROOM SIZE** People need **sufficient room** while they work.	The basic requirements laid down in the Workplace Regulations must **always be exceeded,** particularly if space is taken up by plant and equipment.
11	**WORKSTATIONS AND SEATING** People need to be able to work in **adequate comfort** (including protection from the weather), and able to work without strain.	Mainly operational in intent – but designers who become involved in designing workstations and work processes need to have **expertise in ergonomics and particularly manual handling and activities which are repetitive or awkward or involve vibration,** or seek help.
12	**FLOORS AND TRAFFIC ROUTES** Workplace floors and walking or vehicle routes need to be **safe and fit for purpose.**	Focused mainly upon *floors having an adequately smooth and low-slip-risk finish and being adequately drained,* with handrails to stairs and ramps, ramps not being too steep and holes being guarded. Walking or vehicle routes to be designed to be clear of obstruction, especially in busy areas/escape routes.
13	**FALLS OR FALLING OBJECTS** People need to be protected from *falls or falling into dangerous places or material falling onto them.*	Covers a range of hazards and the need for: ❑ fencing and toe-boards at edges of floors ❑ fencing or covering of hazardous materials (including those in tanks, pits, vessels etc, and including protection from vapours) ❑ fencing to protect from vehicles ❑ where possible, protection even where there is normally no access ❑ special protection at loading bays etc, to protect from falls while enabling vehicle access, eg by a mechanised system ❑ where possible, staircases rather than ladders ❑ fixed ladders to have max 6 m between landings, with safety hoops and gated access ❑ no fragile materials and roofs or other covers and all such areas to be accessed easily ❑ no changes in level which could cause a fall ❑ safe storage and stacking of materials/products ❑ safe work practices which do not require people to clamber over (eg) flat-bed lorries and loads, ie where they may fall. Some rules-of-thumb are set out.
14	**(GLASS ETC) WINDOWS ETC** People need to be protected from **breakage** and **recognise the risks presented.**	Each situation needs to be **risk assessed** and **suitable materials selected and protection provided.** Some rules-of-thumb are set out.

Table 2.1 *Summary of the Workplace Regulations (cont)*

Reg	Summary of requirements	Notes
15	**OPENING WINDOWS ETC** People need to be protected from *falling out of openings* and *colliding with windows* etc, when open.	Each situation needs to be risk-assessed both for *"in-use" conditions* and during *operation of the open/close mechanism*.
16	**CLEANING WINDOWS ETC** People need to be able to *clean windows* etc, *safely.*	Each situation needs to be risk-assessed, avoiding the need for cleaning (eg self-cleaning glass), or providing the ability to (SFARP) clean from the inside or (failing that) from the outside using suitable equipment (cradles or travelling ladders with attachment for safety harness) and/or fixed safe anchorage points for harnesses or long ladders (6 m to 9 m max). (The use of external mobile equipment is not mentioned).
17	**ORGANISATION OF TRAFFIC ROUTES** People and vehicles need to be able to *circulate safely.* Traffic routes include stairs, ladders, ramps etc, and loading bays together with associated doors and gates.	The Regulations require adequate **provision** as well as **organisation**. The ACoP contains considerable detail on what is a specialist subject. Matters to consider include: ❑ adequate provision and organisation of routes ❑ adequate separation from adjacent work activities ❑ adequate width at doors and gates ❑ separation of pedestrians and vehicles ❑ signing, speed limits, humps etc – various issues ❑ avoidance of obstructions, low head-room etc ❑ provision for DDA requirements including wheelchairs, impaired sight, impaired hearing etc ❑ avoid ladders/steep stairs if possible and especially if they cannot be used safely (including the need to carry loads) ❑ restrict vehicle types to areas where they can operate safely ❑ allow for two-way traffic plus parked vehicles ❑ provide protection from vehicle impact as necessary and protect vehicles at edges, drops etc ❑ protect people from fumes or risk from shed loads ❑ avoid the need to reverse (or take precautions) ❑ avoid trapping hazards – especially with driverless vehicles ❑ physically separate/protect people from vehicles at doorways, tunnels, bridges etc ❑ consider risks where vehicles are loaded/unloaded/ tip etc ❑ consider risks at crossing points and seek grade separation (see particular requirements on this) ❑ consider crowds at start/end of day/shift ❑ consider risks in loading bays; consider refuges.
18	**DOORS AND GATES** They must be safe in use ie *suitably constructed with adequate safety devices* as part of the finished installation.	The Regulations and ACoP point out a range of issues: ❑ if running on tracks, have a device to stop them coming off ❑ if vertically opening, have a device to prevent it falling back down ❑ if powered: (a) have a device to prevent trapping of people and (b) have an emergency cut-out switch and (c) be capable of being opened manually (but safely in the event that power is restored) unless it opens automatically if the power fails. This requirement excludes doors/gates which are there to protect from falls eg lift doors ❑ if it could be pushed open and hit people, have a vision panel (which enables wheelchairs to be seen) ❑ if tools are required for manually operation, they should be available at all times ... and detailed advice is given.
19	**ESCALATORS AND MOVING WALKWAYS** They must *function safely.*	The Regulations note that they must have "any necessary safety devices" and "be fitted with one or more emergency stop controls which are easily identified and readily accessible".

Table 2.1 *Summary of the Workplace Regulations (cont)*

Reg	Summary of requirements	Notes
20	**"SANITARY CONVENIENCES"** ie TOILETS. They are to be *"suitable, sufficient, readily accessible"*.	They must be in adequately-lit and ventilated rooms and provide separate male/female facilities or provide a single-user room which can be secured from the inside. Ensure adequate privacy and also appropriate separation from areas where food is processed, prepared or eaten. Each WC must be in a single-user room which can be secured from the inside. The minimum extent of provision is given in Reg 21, which also sets out the standard of provision (ie drained, flushable, properly-equipped, ventilated, lit and protected from the weather, odours dealt with).
21	WASHING FACILITIES *In addition to being provided at toilets and changing rooms, suitable and sufficient readily-accessible washing facilities, including showers if necessary, are to be provided.*	Appropriate washing facilities (including baths or showers if required by the nature of the work), must be provided at sanitary conveniences and also near changing rooms. Ensure adequate privacy. Basic requirements for provision are: ❑ provide separate male/female facilities or provide a single-user room which can be secured from the inside ❑ sufficient for all to use without undue delay ❑ special provision for disabled people ❑ hot and cold running water with anti-scald mixer ❑ soap or other means of getting clean ❑ towels or other means of drying ❑ ventilated, lit and protected from the weather. Minimum numbers of facilities are set out in detail and guidance given for remote workplaces and temporary worksites. Warning is given about Legionnaire's disease.
22	DRINKING WATER People must be **provided with** *"wholesome drinking water"* which is readily-accessible at suitable places and marked as fit for drinking.	Consider risks of contamination from chemicals, bacteria etc.
23	ACCOMMODATION FOR CLOTHING Provide suitable and sufficient *storage for clothes.*	Consider the need to accommodate both clothing removed on arrival and work clothes removed before departure – separately if there is a contamination risk. Provide storage which enables people to hang clothing in a clean, warm, well-ventilated dry place where it can dry out. Consider the need for secure storage and additional provisions for PPE.
24	FACILITIES FOR CHANGING CLOTHING Provide *changing facilities* if people need to change into special clothing for work and need privacy to do so.	Provide separate facilities for men and women. Consider the risks of cross-contamination. Careful consideration needs to be given to the relationship between changing rooms and other facilities (clothing storage, toilets, workrooms, eating facilities etc). The extent of provision will require a study of possible numbers and work patterns. No specific mention is made of changing (and other facilities) for cyclists, but this could be considered.
25	FACILITIES FOR REST AND TO EAT MEALS Provide *"suitable and sufficient rest facilities at readily accessible places".*	The detailed requirements must be carefully studied, taking account of working conditions, food contamination risks, the particular requirements of pregnant women and nursing mothers and the need to avoid nuisance from tobacco smoke.

3   Information about hazards

The following tables address a range of hazards and provide information to assist understanding and thinking. It is not (and never could be) comprehensive, but should assist in informing designers and helping them to access guidance. *Space is provided for users to add their own notes and references.*

The control measures shown are typical controls which may be chosen and implemented by those managing a workplace.

Physical environment – lighting		
HAZARD		Insufficient light for safe activity; headaches or damage to sight due to prolonged periods in dark spaces or low quality light source. Other problems are glare and flashes.
KEY FEATURES		Levels of lighting, quality of the light, steadiness of the light.
TRIGGERS		Inadequate intensity or quality of light. Excessive light.
BACKGROUND		Adequacy of light is normally assessed using the information provided in the CIBSE Guidance. The medical requirement for daylight appears to be uncertain.
E	ELIMINATION	Inappropriate light conditions can easily be removed as a hazard by making proper provision and/or protection. Incidences of unshielded glare or flash should be eliminated SFARP.
R	REDUCTION	Minimise exposure high/low levels of light.
I	INFORMATION FOR USERS	Warning notices for glare and flash.
	INFORMATION FOR OTHERS	Basis of design statement in the O+M manual. Maintenance requirements set out in the O+M manual.
C	CONTROLS ENVISAGED	Shading and eye protectors for glare and flash.
KEY REFERENCES		❑ CIBSE Code for interior lighting ❑ CIBSE Lighting guide: the industrial environment ❑ CIBSE Lighting guide: areas for visual display terminals ❑ CIBSE Lighting in hostile and hazardous environments ❑ HSE Lighting at work HSG38 ❑ Client requirements.
NOTES		

Physical environment – noise

	HAZARD	Impairment of hearing due to prolonged periods at excessive noise levels or short-term exposure to extreme levels of noise. Lack of audibility. Apart from damage to hearing, noise may contribute to stress-related ill-health and noise may cause annoyance and distraction from other hazards.
	KEY FEATURES	Noise is a common problem with different effects at different frequencies and cumulative over time. It is a specialist subject. The effect of noise sources in the workplace is influenced by the degree of attenuation and transmission between spaces. The required limits on noise will depend on the situation.
	TRIGGERS	Machinery, traffic, processes
	BACKGROUND	Limits on levels of noise in workplaces are stated in the Control of Noise at Work Regulations, with action values and limiting values. The Building Regulations Part E deals with acoustic insulation between domestic spaces and reverberation within certain common spaces and classrooms; these are normally issues of comfort rather than health and safety, although in some circumstances they could cause distraction. Noise may affect adjacent buildings – in which the tolerance of noise may be low (eg hospitals). Requirements for comfort are given in the BSRIA "Rules of Thumb".
E	ELIMINATION	Reduction in noises generated to a safe level or separation of people from excessive levels of noise are the best design options.
R	REDUCTION	The level of risk from residual noise may be reduced by applying appropriate controls.
I	INFORMATION FOR USERS	Advisory notices.
	INFORMATION FOR OTHERS	Noise nuisance management strategy.
C	CONTROLS ENVISAGED	Attenuation measures and barriers. Limiting periods of exposure. Noise monitoring devices which alert people to a rise in noise levels. PPE/noise protectors to protect people's hearing, preferably to be used for short periods only for specific tasks in noisy spaces.
	KEY REFERENCES	❑ Control of Noise at Work Regulations 2005 ❑ HSE website – Topic "noise at work" ❑ CIBSE guide B ❑ HSE Noise at work INDG362 ❑ HSE Noise in engineering EIS26 ❑ Institute of acoustics library through www.ioa.org.uk

NOTES

Physical environment – vibration

HAZARD	Discomfort. Whole-Body Vibration (WBV). Hand-Arm Vibration Syndrome (HAVS) and "white finger". Distraction from various other risks. Damage to fabric, eg fixings coming loose and causing accidents.
KEY FEATURES	Vibration is a risk in certain specific circumstances, mainly industrial. It is a specialist subject. Limits on levels of vibration in workplaces are stated in the Control of Vibration at Work Regulations, with action values and limiting values. Vibrations may affect adjacent buildings – in which the tolerance of vibration may be low (eg hospitals). Remedies include the provision of anti-vibration mounts and dampers.
TRIGGERS	Machinery, tools, traffic, processes.
BACKGROUND	Safe levels of vibration are normally assessed?

E	ELIMINATION	Reduction in vibrations generated to a safe level or separation of people from excessive levels of vibration are the best design options.
R	REDUCTION	The level of risk from residual vibration may be reduced by applying appropriate controls.
I	INFORMATION FOR USERS	Advisory notices.
	INFORMATION FOR OTHERS	Vibration management strategy.
C	CONTROLS ENVISAGED	Attenuation measures eg anti-vibration mounts, dampers, isolation barriers. Vibration monitoring devices which alert people to a rise in levels of vibration. Limited periods of exposure.

KEY REFERENCES	❑ Control of Vibration at Work Regulations 2005 and its ACoP L140. ❑ HSE website – Topic "vibration at work". ❑ HSE Control the risks from hand-arm vibration INDG175. ❑ HSE Whole-body vibration on construction, mining and quarrying machines RR400.
NOTES	

Physical environment – temperature

HAZARD		Physical symptoms and possibly heat-stroke/frost-bite or other severe medical conditions. Worker fatigue/loss of concentration which may cause mistakes which cause accidents. Loss of dexterity which may cause accidents with controls or sharps or hazardous materials etc. Distraction from various other risks.
KEY FEATURES		Thermal comfort is a normal part of building services design. Hot processes, cold stores etc need to be carefully considered, including the effects of any PPE worn by workers.
TRIGGERS		Extreme hot or cold (or less extreme conditions but for prolonged periods) Minimum of 16 degrees Celsius for occupied areas in the ACoP to the Workplace Regulations
BACKGROUND		Normally the temperature range experienced by people is controlled within acceptable levels by heating, ventilation and comfort cooling or air conditioning. Note that ventilation also serves to remove stale air, containing carbon dioxide and other contaminating gases. There are no absolute requirements in the Building or Workplace Regulations for a maximum temperature but the CIBSE "Rules of Thumb" set out suggested limits for design.
E	ELIMINATION	The hazard is normally removed.
R	REDUCTION	The level of risk from residual risks may be reduced by applying appropriate controls.
I	INFORMATION FOR USERS	Advisory notices and thermometers.
	INFORMATION FOR OTHERS	Normally provided within the O+M manual.
C	CONTROLS ENVISAGED	Provision of PPE to keep warm may be appropriate in some circumstances. In extreme conditions (eg cold-stores, furnaces), there could be risk of death and appropriate safeguards (including limited periods of exposure) and alarms need to be designed in. Provision of PPE to keep cool is rare, although local area cooling or PPE may be provided.
KEY REFERENCES		❑ CIBSE Guide B ❑ Building Regulations Part F ❑ Workplace Regulations and ACoP ❑ HSE website: Topic "heat stress" ❑ HSE General ventilation in the workplace: guidance for employers HSG202 ❑ HSE Heat stress in the workplace GEIS1 ❑ CIBSE Air filtration and natural ventilation GS A4 ❑ BSRIA Ventilation effectiveness in mechanical ventilation systems TN 1/88 ❑ BS7915 Ergonomics of the thermal environment: guide to design and evaluation of working practices for cold indoor environments.
NOTES		

Physical environment – wetness and humidity

HAZARD		Presence of moisture as water or dampness or moisture vapour OR absence of moisture.
KEY FEATURES		Can cause medical problems and may exacerbate existing conditions. Moisture can make floors slippery. Dryness can cause drying of the mucous membranes.
TRIGGERS		Exposure to moisture/dryness.
BACKGROUND		In most structures exposure to moisture as water or dampness is designed out. Levels of moisture vapour are normally controlled by ventilation or air conditioning. Moisture drips from condensation or escaping from air conditioners may itself cause slippery floors. The Building Regulations Parts C and F include provisions to exclude entry of moisture and water and to manage it by ventilation.
E	ELIMINATION	The hazards are normally removed.
R	REDUCTION	The level of risk from residual risks may be reduced by applying appropriate controls.
I	INFORMATION FOR USERS	Not normally required.
	INFORMATION FOR OTHERS	May be dealt with within the O+M manual.
C	CONTROLS ENVISAGED	Provision of shields or PPE to keep dry may be appropriate in some circumstances.
KEY REFERENCES		❑ CIBSE Guide B ❑ HSE General ventilation in the workplace HSG 202 ❑ Building Regulations Parts C and F.
NOTES		

Physical environment – draughts

HAZARD		Noticeable movements of air through occupied spaces.
KEY FEATURES		Can cause medical problems.
TRIGGERS		High airflows due to ventilation (including air conditioning) or at openings or local to air-leaks.
BACKGROUND		The avoidance of draughts is normally achieved through seeking to reduce energy consumption for heating.
E	ELIMINATION	In most structures exposure to draughts is designed out.
R	REDUCTION	The risk is normally designed out but if it remains then its effect may be reduced by design of enclosed work spaces (eg cubicles) or screening.
I	INFORMATION FOR USERS	Not normally required.
	INFORMATION FOR OTHERS	Not normally required.
C	CONTROLS ENVISAGED	Provision of special clothing may be appropriate in certain spaces.
KEY REFERENCES		❑ HSE General ventilation in the workplace HSG 202 ❑ Building Regulations Part F.
NOTES		

Chemical and/or biological environment – sanitary conditions

HAZARD		Spread of human bacterial contamination and other sanitary issues such as control of vermin.
KEY FEATURES		Can cause medical problems.
TRIGGERS		Lack of adequate sanitary facilities and inadequate waste storage facilities.
BACKGROUND		Provision of adequate toilets, washing facilities and, where necessary, provision for changing of clothing is required by the Building Regulations Part G and the Workplace Regulations. The Building Regulations also require that solid waste materials can be stored properly.
E	ELIMINATION	Proper facilities should always be provided.
R	REDUCTION	The level of risk is normally reduced SFARP.
I	INFORMATION FOR USERS	Advisory notices.
	INFORMATION FOR OTHERS	In the O+M manual if required.
C	CONTROLS ENVISAGED	In high-risk situations (eg hospitals) measures such as barrier clothing and hand-cleansing gels may be required.
KEY REFERENCES		❑ CIBSE Guide G ❑ Building Regulations Part G ❑ The Workplace Regulations and ACoP ❑ BS6465 for toilets ❑ Infection at work: controlling the risks Dept of Health, Advisory Committee on Dangerous Pathogens (ACDP) ❑ HSE/ACDP Biological agents: Managing the risk in laboratories and healthcare premises Web only (HSE website) ❑ Infection control guidance for care homes DoH.
NOTES		

Chemical and/or biological environment – animals

HAZARD		Presence of animals in spaces occupied or visited by people. Residual risks from dead animals or animal-based products or residues.
KEY FEATURES		Can cause medical problems. Risk of contamination, transfer of parasites etc, allergic reactions, bronchial problems, viral infections etc
TRIGGERS		Presence of insects, vermin, viruses etc.
BACKGROUND		The presence of vermin is normally designed out, although some places are particularly prone to infestation (eg food stores, kitchens, eating areas and closed-off spaces such as lofts). The presence of insects can be designed out to some extent. The presence of other animals (by choice) requires specialist knowledge and management.
E	ELIMINATION	The ingress and support of vermin must be designed out but complete success cannot be guaranteed. Avoid hidden voids which cannot be cleaned out. Avoid materials which can harbour infestation.
R	REDUCTION	Further risk reduction is an "in-use" management issue.
I	INFORMATION FOR USERS	Advisory notices.
	INFORMATION FOR OTHERS	Particular, unusual issues may be dealt with within the O+M manual.
C	CONTROLS ENVISAGED	Design to facilitate inspection and cleaning in high-risk areas.
KEY REFERENCES		❑ CIRIA Working with wildlife C567 ❑ HSE Managing health and safety in zoos Web15 ❑ HSE Anthrax – Guidance booklet HS(G)174 ❑ HSE The management, design and operation of microbiological containment laboratories.
NOTES		

Chemical and/or biological environment – moulds and fungal growths

HAZARD		Presence of moulds and/or fungal growths in spaces occupied or visited by people.
KEY FEATURES		Can cause medical problems. Risk of allergic reaction,
TRIGGERS		Presence of spores, growing medium and supportive environmental conditions.
BACKGROUND		The presence of fungal growths is normally designed out, although some places are particularly prone to outbreaks(eg damp spaces and closed-off spaces such as lofts).
E	ELIMINATION	The ingress and support of fungal growths must be designed out but complete success cannot be guaranteed. Avoid hidden voids which cannot be cleaned out. Avoid materials which can harbour infestation.
R	REDUCTION	Further risk reduction is an "in-use" management issue.
I	INFORMATION FOR USERS	Advisory notices.
	INFORMATION FOR OTHERS	Particular, unusual issues may be dealt with within the O+M manual.
C	CONTROLS ENVISAGED	Design to facilitate inspection and cleaning in high-risk areas.
KEY REFERENCES		❑ BRE Remedial wood preservatives: use them safely Digest 371 ❑ HSE In-situ timber treatment using timber preservatives GS46 ❑ RICS Research on toxic mould (RICS website).
NOTES		

Chemical and/or biological environment – other hazardous materials (solids, liquids, gases, fumes)

HAZARD		Contact with hazardous materials. Spread of escaped liquids and gases. Gases given off during activities such as welding.
KEY FEATURES		Can cause medical problems if liquids or gases escape or are released and are ingested orally or through the skin. May cause allergic reaction. Can cause explosions.
TRIGGERS		All chemicals and other materials of a hazardous nature whether imported or created. Processes or activities which use or release gases or liquids.
BACKGROUND		All hazardous materials need to be considered, in particular where there are industrial processes or experimental work. Gases such as radon or methane emanating from the ground need to be considered. The build-up of gases such as carbon dioxide (from breathing) and of the products of combustion and fuel storage need to be dealt with by proper ventilation and the Building Regulations Parts F and J deal with this. Gases emanating from the structure itself should not be a problem if acceptable materials are used; some solvents have been suspected of causing problems. The Building Regulations Part C deals with the risk from gases from the ground and Part D deals specifically with risks from formaldehyde foam insulation.
E	ELIMINATION	Where possible hazardous materials should be removed from areas accessed by people. Specification of materials which can only be cleaned using hazardous processes or compounds should be avoided.
R	REDUCTION	Substitution of a lower-risk hazard may be possible. The overall final level of risk is normally reduced SFARP.
I	INFORMATION FOR USERS	Advisory notices and test equipment.
	INFORMATION FOR OTHERS	Normally provided within the O+M manual.
C	CONTROLS ENVISAGED	In dangerous situations (eg nuclear) periodic testing may be appropriate and PPE may be needed.
KEY REFERENCES		❑ Building Regulations Parts C,D,F,J ❑ COSHH Regulations and ACoP L5 ❑ COSHH essentials (HSE on-line advice at www.coshh-essentials.org.uk) ❑ HSE Workplace exposure limits (related to COSHH) EH40 ❑ CHIPS Regulations ❑ HSE Environmental hygiene EH series (various topics) ❑ HSE COSHH Essentials for welding, hot work and allied processes WL series (various topics) ❑ Pocket guide to hazardous chemicals by (US) NIOSH ❑ TOXNET Toxicology Data Network (US) National library of medicine ❑ Control of Asbestos Regulations and ACoP L143 ❑ Control and Use of Lead at Work Regulations and ACoP L132 ❑ Ionising Radiation Regulations and ACoP L121 ❑ The Gas Appliances (Safety) Regulations 1995 ❑ Gas Safety (Installation and Use) Regulations 1998 and AcoP L56 ❑ HSE General ventilation in the workplace: guidance for employers HSG202 ❑ HSE Introduction to local exhaust ventilation HSG37 ❑ CIBSE Air filtration and Natural Ventilation GS A4 ❑ TRADA Wood preservation – chemicals and processes. **NOTE:** The HSE has published a wide range of guidance notes on this subject – see HSE website for further information.
NOTES		

Chemical and/or biological environment – pollution (smoke)

HAZARD		Creation and spread of smoke (ie air-borne particles and gases).
KEY FEATURES		Smoke created deliberately or accidentally can cause medical problems if gases and particles escape or are released and are ingested orally or through the skin. May cause allergic reaction. Can cause blindness and incapacity in an emergency situation.
TRIGGERS		Processes or activities which release smoke (as well as fire).
BACKGROUND		The presence of smoke is normally considered in particular industrial processes or experimental work – and in smoking, which is now recognised as dangerous.
E	ELIMINATION	Where possible smoke should be removed from areas accessed by people. Dusts should be screened before emission.
R	REDUCTION	For process situations substitution of a lower-risk hazard may be possible; for accidental situations, use of materials which are less combustible or which give off less dense smoke or less dangerous gases and particles may be appropriate. The level of risk is normally reduced SFARP.
I	INFORMATION FOR USERS	Advisory notices and test equipment.
	INFORMATION FOR OTHERS	Normally provided within the O+M manual.
C	CONTROLS ENVISAGED	In dangerous process situations periodic testing of the air may be appropriate and PPE may be needed. Control of accidental fire situations – see FIRE below. Risks to environment to be managed by analysis of chimney height and flume behaviour.
KEY REFERENCES		❏ Building Regulations Parts B,F ❏ BSEN 12101 Smoke and heat control systems.
NOTES		

Chemical and/or biological environment – pollution (dusts and fibres)

HAZARD		Spread of dusts and fibres.
KEY FEATURES		Can cause medical problems if dust particles become airborne or contaminate clothing and are ingested orally or through the skin. May cause allergic reaction or cancer. Dust/air mixtures may be explosive – see EXPLOSION below.
TRIGGERS		Processes or activities which use or release dusts or fibres. **NOTE:** if in doubt, research the subject, including agricultural products, wood products, cement, stone, silica, etc.
BACKGROUND		The presence of dusts or fibres is normally considered in particular industrial processes or experimental work. However, asbestos must always be borne in mind and dealt with in accordance with the latest regulations and guidance.
E	ELIMINATION	Whenever possible dangerous dust should be removed from areas accessed by people.
R	REDUCTION	The level of risk is normally reduced SFARP although in the case of specific materials such as lead, asbestos and nuclear materials, legal requirements must be met.
I	INFORMATION FOR USERS	Advisory notices and test equipment.
	INFORMATION FOR OTHERS	Normally provided within the O+M manual.
C	CONTROLS ENVISAGED	In dangerous situations (eg nuclear) periodic testing of dust may be appropriate and PPE may be needed. Periods of exposure may be limited. Oxygen monitors may be provided.
KEY REFERENCES		❑ Control of Asbestos Regulations 2006 and ACoP L143 ❑ HSE Management of asbestos in buildings HSG 227 ❑ Control and Use of Lead at Work Regulations and ACoP L132 ❑ Ionising Radiation Regulations and ACoP L121 ❑ COSHH Regulations and ACoP L5 ❑ HSE Dust: general principles of protection EH44 ❑ HSE Various dusts – EH series search on HSE website ❑ HSE Summary criteria for occupational exposure limits EH64.
NOTES		

Chemical and/or biological environment – other contamination/pollution

HAZARD		Chemical or bacterial contamination.
KEY FEATURES		Can cause medical problems if fine particles are spread and contaminate clothing etc, and are ingested orally or through the skin. May cause allergic reaction.
TRIGGERS		Presence of contamination in air, soils, ground-water, raw materials. Materials, processes or activities which release particles or sprays. Lack of safe processes or use of inappropriate surfaces.
BACKGROUND		Testing for contamination is required wherever it may be introduced. Safe methods for using surfaces have been developed in the food industry and in specialist areas such as laboratories. Control of pollution from the ground is dealt with in the Building Regulations Part C. Bacterial contamination includes Legionellosis. This is a specialist subject.
E	ELIMINATION	It may be possible to remove a potential source of contamination.
R	REDUCTION	Substitution of a lower-risk hazard may be possible. The level of risk is normally reduced SFARP and statutory or advised limits must be respected.
I	INFORMATION FOR USERS	For residual risks, advisory notices and test equipment.
	INFORMATION FOR OTHERS	Normally provided within the O+M manual.
C	CONTROLS ENVISAGED	In dangerous situations, periodic testing may be appropriate. Systems may be made safer to reduce risks of spillage, particularly during maintenance, eg by providing for isolation of runs. PPE may be needed.
KEY REFERENCES		❑ CIRIA Assessing risks posed by hazardous gases to buildings C659 ❑ Contaminated land research reports Environment Agency ❑ DEFRA and Environment Agency website guidance ❑ CIBSE Minimising the risk of legionnaire's disease TM13 ❑ Building Regulations Part C ❑ HSE Legionnaire's disease: the control of legionella bacteria in water systems, ACoP L8 ❑ HSE COSHH and its ACoP L5 ❑ HSE COSHH essentials: easy steps to control chemicals HSG193 ❑ HSE Monitoring strategies for toxic substances ❑ HSE Biological monitoring of the workplace HSG167 ❑ HSE Control and Use of Lead at Work Regulations and ACoP L132. Industry-related regulations may apply – eg catering, laboratories, farming.
NOTES		

Hazardous systems – electricity

HAZARD		Electrical shock.
KEY FEATURES		Causing death or injury.
TRIGGERS		Contact with live wiring or equipment. Discharge of static electricity.
BACKGROUND		In the UK, The requirements of BS7671 have to be complied with and the Building Regulations Part P apply to dwellings.
E	ELIMINATION	Removal of electrical systems is not feasible – but in high-risk areas (wet, explosive gases or dusts) special measures must be taken.
R	REDUCTION	Low voltage electricity systems.
I	INFORMATION FOR USERS	Advisory notices.
	INFORMATION FOR OTHERS	An essential part of the O+M manual.
C	CONTROLS ENVISAGED	Special fittings, double insulation, locked cabinets, interlocks and isolation systems etc.
KEY REFERENCES		❑ Building Regulations Part P ❑ Electricity at Work Regulations 1989 ❑ HSE Memorandum of guidance on the electricity at work regulations HSR 25 ❑ BS7671 Requirements for electrical installations: IEE wiring regulations ❑ IEE wiring regulations – explained and illustrated (Butterworth) ❑ HSE Electricity at work – safe working practices HSG85 ❑ NICEIC Technical manual and other guidance ❑ BS5958 Code of Practice for the control of static electricity ❑ CIBSE guide K.
NOTES		

Hazardous systems – hot water and steam (and steam condensate)

HAZARD		Excessively hot water (above 43 degrees Celsius) or steam. Steam condensate may be at high temperature (and pressure).
KEY FEATURES		Can cause severe burns, scalds and death. Steam burns twice, on contact and on condensing, causing deep burns. In industrial situations, steam is usually under pressure and temperatures can be over 100 degrees Celsius. Hot water assists legionella growth.
TRIGGERS		Contact with excessively hot water or steam.
BACKGROUND		Limit temperatures of free water and steam are normally set so as not to cause problems unless there is an accidental escape.
E	ELIMINATION	Not normally possible.
R	REDUCTION	Protection against accidental escape should be to a high level of reliability. Reliance upon controls is not recommended.
I	INFORMATION FOR USERS	Warning signs where appropriate.
	INFORMATION FOR OTHERS	Instructions for maintenance and operation.
C	CONTROLS ENVISAGED	Protective shields, PPE.
KEY REFERENCES		❑ BP Safety Group: Hazards of Steam (BP process safety series).
NOTES		

Hazardous systems – piped gases/liquids

HAZARD		Dangerous gases and liquids. Vacuum/suction lines and systems.
KEY FEATURES		Injury, medical conditions or death.
TRIGGERS		Escape of dangerous gases/liquids. Blasting with carried materials eg grit.
BACKGROUND		Expertise in the handling of gases/liquids resides within specialist companies. Liquids may add to electrical hazards eg drains running through switch rooms.
E	ELIMINATION	Not normally possible.
R	REDUCTION	Protection against accidental escape should be to a high level of reliability.
I	INFORMATION FOR USERS	Routing drawings, physical identification and isolation points. Warning signs where appropriate.
	INFORMATION FOR OTHERS	Instructions for maintenance and operation.
C	CONTROLS ENVISAGED	Provision of masks and breathing apparatus in extreme situations. Eye wash, safety showers. Provision of alarms. Physical shrouding to protect from damage (particularly when exposed but also for protection of pipes carrying dangerous gases, even within walls and pipe-ways).
KEY REFERENCES		❑ BP process safety group: various titles ❑ Energy Institute: Model codes of practice in the petroleum industry ❑ HSE Assessing the risk from gasoline pipelines in the UK based on a review of historical experience CRR 210 ❑ HSE Further guidance on emergency plans for major accident hazard pipelines: the pipeline safety regulations.

NOTES

Hazardous systems – hot/cold surfaces

HAZARD		Excessively hot surfaces (above 43 degrees Celsius). Excessively cold surfaces.
KEY FEATURES		Can cause severe burns (including cryogenic burns) and death. The young, elderly and infirm are at particular risk.
TRIGGERS		Contact with excessively hot or cold surfaces.
BACKGROUND		Limit temperatures of surfaces accessible to the touch are normally set so as not to cause problems unless there is an accidental escape.
E	ELIMINATION	Surfaces which do not need to be exposed should be covered/insulated/lagged.
R	REDUCTION	Protection against accidental touching should be to a high level of reliability.
I	INFORMATION FOR USERS	Warning signs where appropriate.
	INFORMATION FOR OTHERS	Instructions for maintenance and operation.
C	CONTROLS ENVISAGED	Provision of PPE may be appropriate.
KEY REFERENCES		❑ RoSPA Home safety topic briefing on burns and scald injuries HS40.
NOTES		

Hazardous systems – storage

HAZARD		Storage of materials presents three main areas of hazard; the materials themselves, the strength and stability of the storage system and the risks involved in the loading and unloading of materials into and out of storage.
KEY FEATURES		Storage systems involve a wide range of situations, including the storage and maintenance (often at height) of materials and products which may be hazardous, heavy or unwieldy and which may contain stored energy which may be accidentally released.
TRIGGERS		Working outside process. Unforeseen circumstances.
BACKGROUND		Storage is an area of activity in which everyone participates. In some circumstances there are experts involved, designing and constructing customised solutions, but in many situations a storage scenario will be set by others. The challenge under CDM is for the design team to address storage situations to minimise risks to users.
E	ELIMINATION	Significantly hazardous storage scenarios should be avoided SFARP.
R	REDUCTION	Risks must be minimised by informed choices.
I	INFORMATION FOR USERS	Informative notices and warning signs where appropriate.
	INFORMATION FOR OTHERS	Instructions for maintenance and operation.
C	CONTROLS ENVISAGED	Signage. Access equipment. PPE as a last resort only as it will be mislaid.
KEY REFERENCES		❑ HSE Dangerous Substances and Explosive Atmosphere Regulations and ACoP L135: Storage of dangerous substances ❑ HSE Chemical warehousing: The storage of packaged dangerous substances HSG71 ❑ HSE Chemical storage tank systems: good practice: guidance on design, manufacture, installation, operation, inspection C598 ❑ HSE The storage of flammable liquids in containers HSG51 ❑ HSE The storage of flammable liquids in tanks HSG176 ❑ HSE The spraying of flammable liquids HSG178 ❑ HSE Handling and stacking of bales INDG125 ❑ HSE Container terminals: safe working practice HSG7 ❑ HSE H&S in retail and wholesale warehouses HSG76.
NOTES		

Normal activities – posture and manual handling

HAZARD		Musculo-skeletal injuries and complaints.
KEY FEATURES		Arising from poor posture, awkward movements, excessive loads which overload the human frame. Normally accumulative and can lead to long-term ill-health. Excessive repetition of simple movements may trigger Repetitive Strain Injury (RSI), eg using computers (display screen equipment). Difficult physical tasks may be associated with slips, trips and falls due to loss of balance and/or concentration. Excessive carrying distances increases risk of grip being lost so that loads shift or are dropped, spilled or splashed. Usually associated with discomfort, but not necessarily (eg RSI which can become severe with little warning).
TRIGGERS		Repeated activity involving poor posture, awkward movements, excessive loads; bad "fit" between people and the workplace and/or excessive repetition.
BACKGROUND		Rarely seriously considered until recent times. May be associated with other hazards. Ergonomics is a specialist subject but most injuries and ill-health arise from common activities which are well-explained in HSE guidance, particularly carrying excessive weights in the wrong manner. Design of work areas should reflect functionality and fit – for example, kitchens should be designed with easily-accessed storage and lay-down areas for hot/heavy pans etc adjacent to hobs and ovens; there should be adequate circulation space.
E	**ELIMINATION**	Tasks may be changed and some may be mechanised. If the workplace and tasks are well-designed, the hazard may be eliminated.
R	**REDUCTION**	Levels of risk may be reduced by reducing loads and frequency or by providing equipment.
I	**INFORMATION FOR USERS**	Informative notices.
	INFORMATION FOR OTHERS	An outline policy for ergonomics may explain the approach assumed by designers. Note that workplace management will carry out their own in-use assessments and the policy may be amended. For particular inherent workplace activities, information on limitations should be provided to management.
C	**CONTROLS ENVISAGED**	Mechanical aids, platforms etc to make tasks easier. Manual handling risk assessments. Health surveillance. Training.
KEY REFERENCES		❑ Display Screen Equipment Regulations and ACoP L26 ❑ Manual Handling Regulations and ACoP L23 ❑ LOLER and ACoP L113 ❑ HSE Visual display units (book) 1983 ❑ HSE Working with VDUs INDG36 and guidance L23 ❑ HSE Seating at work HSG57 ❑ HSE Backs for the future HSG149 ❑ HSE Understanding ergonomics at work INDG90.
NOTES		

Normal activities – use of vehicles

HAZARD		Collision and trapping of drivers and people by vehicles, including forklift trucks and robotic transfer vehicles.
KEY FEATURES		Death or injury.
TRIGGERS		Operator error, impaired sight-lines, toppling over, other accidents *per se*.
BACKGROUND		The Building Regulations Part K deal with some matters relating to vehicles and the Workplace Regulations also contain wide-ranging detailed requirements.
E	ELIMINATION	Hazards should be removed SFARP, preferably by removing people from dangerous situations, ie segregation.
R	REDUCTION	Less risky options may exist and should be considered. Risks may be reduced, eg by providing clearly-defined pedestrian routes or by adding fail-safe controls.
I	INFORMATION FOR USERS	Advisory notices.
	INFORMATION FOR OTHERS	Circulation strategy in the O+M manual.
C	CONTROLS ENVISAGED	Various controls such as guards, warning signs, signals, horns etc may be appropriate.
KEY REFERENCES		❑ Building Regulations Part K ❑ Workplace Regulations and ACoP L24 ❑ HSE Road transport in factories and similar workplaces GS9 ❑ HSE Use of vehicles HSG47 ❑ HSE Road transport in factories and similar workplaces GS9 ❑ HSE Managing vehicle safety at the workplace INDG199 ❑ HSE Improving the safety of workers in the vicinity of mobile plant RR358 ❑ HSE Safety in working with lift trucks HSG6 ❑ HSE Lift trucks in potentially flammable atmospheres HSG113.
NOTES		

Normal activities – use of plant and equipment

HAZARD		A wide range of hazardous activity involving the use of blades, presses and other machinery, vehicles (see also above), access equipment, lifting equipment etc.
KEY FEATURES		Each activity carries hazards both in respect of normal activity and situations which can arise when people have accidents or forget to wear PPE etc.
TRIGGERS		Equipment malfunction, abuse, accident etc.
BACKGROUND		The use of plant and equipment is legislated for in some areas of activity but in every situation the hazards need to be identified and the risks assessed. The "LOLER" regulations relate to lifting activities (Lifting Operations and Lifting Equipment Regulations) and the "PUWER" regulations relate to equipment in general (Provision and Use of Work Equipment Regulations).
E	ELIMINATION	Hazards should be removed SFARP, preferably by removing people from dangerous situations.
R	REDUCTION	Less risky options may exist and should be considered. Risks may be reduced eg by adding fail-safe controls.
I	INFORMATION FOR USERS	Advisory notices.
	INFORMATION FOR OTHERS	Normally provided within the O+M manual.
C	CONTROLS ENVISAGED	Various controls such as guards, PPE, warning signs etc may be appropriate.
KEY REFERENCES		❑ Lifting Operations and Lifting Equipment Regulations (LOLER) ❑ Provision and Use of Work Equipment Regulations (PUWER) ❑ Suspended access equipment PM30 ❑ HSE Dangerous Substances and Explosive Atmosphere Regulations and ACoP L134: Design of plant, equipment and workplaces **NOTE:** The HSE has published a wide range of guidance notes on this subject – see HSE website for further information.
NOTES		

Normal activities – industrial processes

HAZARD		There are hazards inherent in some industrial processes.
KEY FEATURES		Each activity carries hazards both in respect of normal activity and situations which can arise when the process goes out of control.
TRIGGERS		Events such as fatigue, corrosion, unstable reactions, contaminated materials, fluid leakage etc.
BACKGROUND		These risks may be managed as part of the operation but design of a new or adapted structure may provide opportunities to reduce overall risks.
E	ELIMINATION	Hazardous processes should be avoided SFARP.
R	REDUCTION	Less risky options may exist and should be considered. Risks may be reduced eg by adding fail-safe controls.
I	INFORMATION FOR USERS	Alarms, advisory notices, safe escape routes, PPE.
	INFORMATION FOR OTHERS	Normally provided within the O+M manual. May include outputs from HAZAN/HAZOP studies.
C	CONTROLS ENVISAGED	Various controls such as monitoring systems may be appropriate.
KEY REFERENCES		❑ HSE Control of Major Accident Hazards Regulations (COMAH) ❑ HSE Safe use and handling of flammable liquids HSG140 ❑ HSE Working safely with solvents INDG273 ❑ HSE Safety in pressure systems. **NOTE:** The HSE has published a wide range of guidance notes on this subject (in particular Engineering information sheets, EIS series) – see HSE website for further information.

NOTES

Normal activities – use of doors and windows/ glazing

HAZARD		Use of doors and windows, skylights and ventilators; brittle materials.
KEY FEATURES		May cause impact damage, trapping of fingers, cuts if glass breaks, falls from height.
TRIGGERS		Accidents, inconsiderate use, horseplay. Presence of fragile materials in rooflights.
BACKGROUND		Safe doors and windows are well covered in the Building Regulations Part K and the Workplace Regulations. Glass and the manifestation of glass is covered by the Building Regulations Parts M and N. Particular care is needed in buildings used by children and young people. Issues arising during refurbishment require particular attention to provide modern levels of protection.
E	ELIMINATION	May be appropriate in certain situations.
R	REDUCTION	Substitution of less fragile materials may be appropriate. Reduction of risks SFARP is always necessary.
I	INFORMATION FOR USERS	Users may need to be alerted to risks of impact as doors open or where glass is used.
	INFORMATION FOR OTHERS	Normally provided within the O+M manual.
C	CONTROLS ENVISAGED	Window opening may need to be restricted at height and hinges may need to be covered in schools or other places where there may be horseplay.
KEY REFERENCES		❑ CIRIA Report 632 Glazing at Height and the standards referred to therein ❑ Building Regulations Parts K, M and N ❑ Workplace Regulations and ACoP L24 ❑ BS8213:Part 1: 1991 Windows,doors and rooflights: design for safety in use and during cleaning of windows, including door-height windows and roof windows (code of practice).
NOTES		

Normal activities – use of lifts, escalators and moving walkways

HAZARD		Use of lifts, escalators and moving walkways.
KEY FEATURES		May cause impact damage, trapping of fingers. Detailed requirements are given in British Standards.
TRIGGERS		Accidents, inconsiderate use, horseplay, breakdown, vandalism.
BACKGROUND		Lifts are covered in the Building Regulations Part M and provision of escalators and moving walkways is included in the Workplace Regulations. Particular care is needed in buildings used by children and young people.
E	ELIMINATION	There is little information on which to make judgements.
R	REDUCTION	Installations should be very safe to use.
I	INFORMATION FOR USERS	Advisory notices for users.
	INFORMATION FOR OTHERS	Normally provided within the O+M manual.
C	CONTROLS ENVISAGED	Cut-outs should be provided to enable users to cut off power in the event of an accident.
KEY REFERENCES		❑ CIBSE Guide D ❑ Building Regulations Part M ❑ HSE Safety in the use of escalators PM34 ❑ BS5656 escalator and moving walks inc Part 2: Safety rules for the construction and installation of escalators and passenger conveyors. Code of practice for the selection, installation and location of new escalators and moving walks ❑ HSE Ergonomic aspects of escalators in retail organisations CRR12.
NOTES		

Slips and trips while in motion on floors and ramps

HAZARD		Accidental slipping or tripping due to a variety of contributory factors.
KEY FEATURES		Injury and possibly death (either immediately or later).
TRIGGERS		Smooth or polished surfaces, presence of contaminants including water, trip hazards, inappropriate footwear, pedestrian behaviour, visual and noise distraction, trailing leads etc, inappropriate or insufficient cleaning, low lighting levels or glare, or smooth flooring adjacent to safe flooring.
BACKGROUND		Clear requirements are given in the Workplace Regulations 1992 and the HSE provides advice, including sponsoring the CIRIA report referenced below. The Building Regulations Parts K and M refer for ramps.
E	ELIMINATION	By good design, the hazard can be eliminated or reduced considerably eg provision of safety flooring in predictably wet areas, adequate electrical and IT sockets to avoid trailing leads. Close attention to building tolerances especially at expansion joints, control joints and thresholds. Specify high-quality floor boxes which will not distort and present a trip hazard. Ramps are higher risk than flat floors and need to be treated carefully with good visual contrast.
R	REDUCTION	Lower risk floor finishes should always be used. For a given floor type, risks may be reduced by good management and attention to the trigger features listed above.
I	INFORMATION FOR USERS	Visual signing by colour change, especially for ramps.
	INFORMATION FOR OTHERS	Cleaning and maintenance requirements must be in the O+M manual.
C	CONTROLS ENVISAGED	Keep flooring in good low-slip-risk condition, by keeping dry and free from trip hazards. Manage cables and hoses.
KEY REFERENCES		❏ Building Regulations Parts K and M ❏ Workplace Regulations and ACoP L24 ❏ CIRIA publication C652 *Safer surfaces to walk on – reducing the risk of slipping* ❏ HSE Website: Topic "Slips and trips" and Slip Assessment Tool ❏ HSE Preventing slips and trips at work INDG225 ❏ Centre for Accessible Environments (CAE) Guidance.
NOTES		

Slips and trips while using stairs and escalators

HAZARD		Falls while negotiating stairs.
KEY FEATURES		Injury and possibly death (either immediately or later).
TRIGGERS		As for slips and trips (slippery surface, presence of contaminants including water, trip hazards, inappropriate footwear, pedestrian behaviour, visual and noise distraction, trailing leads etc) but note that the consequences of falling on stairs are greater.
BACKGROUND		Clear requirements are given in the Workplace Regulations and the Building Regulations Parts K and M. Advice generally as for floors and ramps above – but noting the greater risks on stairs.
E	ELIMINATION	Design for single storey or introduce ramps instead, where possible.
R	REDUCTION	Escalators or lifts may be considered. Stairs should be designed to be as safe as possible.
I	INFORMATION FOR USERS	Clearly visible tread edges.
	INFORMATION FOR OTHERS	Cleaning and maintenance requirements must be in the O+M manual.
C	CONTROLS ENVISAGED	Provision of handrails (Mandatory under the Building Regulations).
KEY REFERENCES		❑ Building Regulations Parts K and M ❑ Workplace Regulations and ACoP L24 ❑ CIRIA Report C652, *Safer surfaces to walk on – reducing the risk of slipping* ❑ HSE Website: Topic "Slips and trips" and Slip Assessment Tool ❑ HSE Preventing slips and trips at work INDG225 ❑ BS5395 Stairs ladders and walkways ❑ BS4211 Specification for permanently fixed ladders ❑ BS4592 Industrial type flooring and stair treads.
NOTES		

Abnormal events – explosion

HAZARD	Pressure wave and high-velocity missiles, flames and gases.
KEY FEATURES	Causes immediate injury and death.
TRIGGERS	Failure of a pressure vessel during testing or in use; loss of control of a process or stored material; ignition of gases or dusts; terrorism and war.
BACKGROUND	Normally considered in particular industrial processes or experimental work or where hazardous materials (including gases) are employed or stored.

E	ELIMINATION	Hazards should be removed SFARP, preferably by removing people from dangerous situations.
R	REDUCTION	Less risky options may exist and should be considered. Risks may be reduced eg by adding fail-safe controls and alarms or providing vented enclosure.
I	INFORMATION FOR USERS	Advisory notices.
	INFORMATION FOR OTHERS	Normally provided within the O+M manual.
C	CONTROLS ENVISAGED	Various controls such as barriers, PPE, warning signs etc may be appropriate.

KEY REFERENCES	
	❑ ATEX: Compliance with the EU "ATEX" Directive 94/9/EC (from HSE and SHAPA, the Solids Handling Association) ❑ HSE Safe handling of combustible dusts: Precautions against explosions HSG103 ❑ HSE Dispensing petrol: Assessing and controlling the risk of fire and explosion at sites where petrol is stored and dispensed as a fuel HSG146 ❑ HSE Design of plant, equipment and workplaces: Dangerous Substances and Explosives Atmospheres Regulations 2002. Approved Code of Practice and Guidance L134 ❑ HSE Storage of dangerous substances: Dangerous Substances and Explosives Atmospheres Regulations 2002. Approved Code of Practice and Guidance L135 ❑ HSE Control and mitigation measures: Dangerous Substances and Explosive Atmospheres Regulations 2002. Approved Code of Practice and Guidance L136 ❑ HSE Manufacture and storage of explosives: Manufacture and Storage of Explosives Regulations 2005. Approved Code of Practice and Guidance L139 ❑ HSE Fire and explosion: how safe is your workplace? INDG370 ❑ HSE The selection, installation and maintenance of electrical equipment for use in and around buildings containing explosives PM82 **NOTE:** The HSE has published a wide range of guidance notes on this subject – see HSE website for further information.

NOTES

Abnormal events – falling objects

	HAZARD	Injury from falling objects.
	KEY FEATURES	Cause injury or death.
	TRIGGERS	Loss of control of material stored or being carried, or failure of overhead structures.
	BACKGROUND	Proper control of stored materials is required, with planning and management to avoid misplacement, instability and overloading. The Workplace Regulations provide sound guidance. Trees may present a hazard.
E	ELIMINATION	Protection should be provided where there is a risk. Ideally heavier materials should be stored on the ground.
R	REDUCTION	Lower risk options should be explored. Risks may be reduced by design of storage systems and transport arrangements.
I	INFORMATION FOR USERS	Advisory notices and electronic reporting
	INFORMATION FOR OTHERS	Storage and transportation strategy and details should be provided within the O+M manual
C	CONTROLS ENVISAGED	Advisory notices and electronic monitoring
	KEY REFERENCES	❑ Building Regulations Part K ❑ Work at Height Regulations ❑ HSE Work at Height Regulations – A brief guide INDG401 ❑ DETR Principles of tree-hazard assessment and management

NOTES

Abnormal events – disproportionate collapse

HAZARD		Structural collapse of a severe nature due to failure of critical members due to a local event.
KEY FEATURES		Loss of life or injury due to partial or complete collapse of a structure.
TRIGGERS		Impact (eg from a vehicle), explosion (eg from gas), failure of a key member (eg due to fatigue or corrosion).
BACKGROUND		Part A of the Building Regulations requires that this risk is considered in occupied buildings. Class A and B buildings may follow a prescribed route which may be appropriate for some situations; otherwise, a risk assessment approach is required.
E	ELIMINATION	Some risks can be removed by for example protecting a building from impact or not using gas.
R	REDUCTION	Selecting a framing system which has load-spreading ability should a key member fail will reduce the risks. Key members must be well tied into the building; they may also be over-sized.
I	INFORMATION FOR USERS	Not applicable.
	INFORMATION FOR OTHERS	The approach taken, the evaluation of risks and the design precautions taken should be recorded with the structural design information passed to the owner.
C	CONTROLS ENVISAGED	Requirements for inspection and maintenance should be clearly recorded.
KEY REFERENCES		❑ Building Regulations Part A ❑ NHBC Technical guidance note: The Building Regulations 2004 edition – England and Wales: requirement A3 – disproportionate collapse ❑ BDA Masonry design for disproportionate collapse requirements under Regulation A3 of the Building Regulations (England & Wales) ❑ SCI Guidance on meeting the robustness requirements in Approved Document A P341 ❑ Seabrook, C Using the building regulations. Part A: structure [Architectural Press, due for publication 2007].
NOTES		

Abnormal events – drowning and asphyxiation

	HAZARD	Drowning and asphyxiation of people.
	KEY FEATURES	Loss of life due to failure to breath, either instantaneously or over time as the lungs are crushed.
	TRIGGERS	Falling into water or powders etc or being buried by collapsing materials. Flooding. Entry into confined spaces which may not support life. Release of gases from gas suppression systems for fire control.
	BACKGROUND	There are a range of risks such as falling into vats of water or powders, or being buried by grain etc during cleaning or trying to release blockages. The challenge is often to stop operatives entering dangerous situations.
E	ELIMINATION	People must be separated from such hazards.
R	REDUCTION	Controls to be provided where possible.
I	INFORMATION FOR USERS	Advisory notices eg "Do not enter silo unless empty – you may be buried and die – the grain will suck you under".
	INFORMATION FOR OTHERS	Separation and escape strategy should be provided within the O+M manual.
C	CONTROLS ENVISAGED	Confined spaces designed as securable/lockable environments with access controlled under permit/authority system. Provision of PPE and developed emergency escape system if entry is vital.
	KEY REFERENCES	❏ Confined Spaces Regulations and ACoP L101 ❏ HSE Safe work in confined spaces INDG258

NOTES

Abnormal events – crowding

HAZARD		Large numbers of people behaving as a crowd.
KEY FEATURES		Normally the behaviour is self-controlled but in some circumstances such as panic, crush or escape crowd behaviour can present a hazard.
TRIGGERS		Large numbers of people gathered in one space; an event which causes them to lose normal inhibitions and act as a group, normally for self-preservation but sometimes for other purposes such as excitement.
BACKGROUND		Crowd behaviour is a phenomenon which experienced frequently in some places such as sports events but can occur elsewhere such as nightclubs. Advice on strength of barriers is provided in Building Regulatons Part K. Crowd flow may be modelled in a computer.
E	ELIMINATION	Crowd behaviour cannot be entirely avoided.
R	REDUCTION	Crowds are less prone to uncontrolled behaviour if they are restrained in smaller groups and if the triggers are managed out.
I	INFORMATION FOR USERS	Signs are unlikely to be read; a good public address system may enable a crowd to be managed positively, overcoming rumour spread by word of mouth.
	INFORMATION FOR OTHERS	A crowd management strategy should be provided in the O+M manual.
C	CONTROLS ENVISAGED	Barriers are used to break up crowd packing and movement. Planning crowd escape routes along level surfaces without steps or street furniture etc will reduce accidents. Rapid easy egress from spaces must be provided, eg emergency escape doors.
KEY REFERENCES		❑ Building Regulations Part K for staircases ❑ HSE Managing crowds safely ❑ Rail Safety and Standards Board Good Practice Guide on Crowd Management ❑ Guide to safety at sports grounds (Department of National Heritage/Scottish Office).
NOTES		

Abnormal events – malicious human intervention

HAZARD		Terrorism, vandalism, crime, arson, illicit use of drugs including tobacco etc.
KEY FEATURES		Unpredictable and widely varying in scope and scale, leading to a variety of hazards.
TRIGGERS		Malicious acts.
BACKGROUND		The issues to be considered are many and varied.
E	ELIMINATION	Not entirely possible but certain security measures may be taken to reduce the chance of an occurrence.
R	REDUCTION	Not certain but certain defensive measures may be taken to reduce the impact of an occurrence.
I	INFORMATION FOR USERS	Not normally applicable.
	INFORMATION FOR OTHERS	Possibly in a confidential document held by particular senior staff.
C	CONTROLS ENVISAGED	The use of controls to reduce risk is widespread but most controls can be circumvented.
KEY REFERENCES		❑ CIRIA publiction SP91, *Dealing with vandalism* ❑ Home office guidance
NOTES		

4 Tables of information about typical workplaces

This section explores some of the workplace issues which arise in a small selection of the many thousands of different workplaces which exist.

The examples given are not meant to be exhaustive or general but are indicative only. Designers of each individual structure will have to consider the various potential hazards which exist in their project and deal with them accordingly.

The following workplaces are discussed on the following pages:

- ❑ a city-centre office block
- ❑ a maternity hospital
- ❑ a prison cell block
- ❑ a stretch of rural motorway
- ❑ a school for infants
- ❑ a food processing plant.

A city-centre office block

FEATURES	THEIR IMPLICATIONS	DISCUSSION
Normal working conditions within the block are low-risk.		While an office is, at first sight, a low-risk environment, it must be borne in mind that there will be a wide range of behaviours exhibited. The population within will be fluid and any training will soon be forgotten. The behaviour of visitors will mainly be uncontrolled.
Specific hazards may however exist which arise from the aspects of cleaning and maintenance which, if not designed for, may affect those who work in and visit the building.	Need to consider how all cleaning and maintenance can be achieved in a safe manner.	
Fire hazards (and other related hazards such as terrorism) will need careful consideration and evacuation procedures designed for.	How can large numbers of people be safely evacuated? Where can they safely be accommodated without risk from traffic?	Maintenance activity will be an ongoing issue as it may affect people generally and certainly the resident contacts for access arrangements. Risks will be minimised if maintenance tasks are easy to access and carry out. The need for access to roofs should be minimised and tasks such as gutter clearance made simple and safe by careful planning of the roofscape so that the need for access beyond safety railings is rarely necessary.
Water stored or used externally eg in a cooling tower must be designed to minimise risk of Legionaire's Disease from air-borne sprays.	Reliance upon maintenance activity should be avoided if possible as there is alays a risk of error or omission.	
Inevitably there will be areas which are hazardous to people if they can gain access.	Access to roofs and other hazardous areas will be abused if it is possible.	Security issues should be carefully addressed so that risks of unauthorised access to roofs and other hazardous areas is controlled.
Areas accessed only for maintenance may be seen as of secondary importance.	If access to plant-rooms etc is difficult, there will be a tendency to skimp on the work.	

Sources of advice: *The British Council for Offices (BCO) publications including* BCO Guide 2005 – Best Practice in the Specification of Offices.

NOTES

A maternity hospital

FEATURES	THEIR IMPLICATIONS	DISCUSSION
All hospitals need to be designed taking account of the patient profile and the nature of the work undertaken. In a maternity hospital, mothers and staff will need safe surroundings.	Issues of cleanliness and contamination hazards will be important. Hazards such as slipping or tripping must also be carefully addressed.	Not only is a maternity hospital a high-risk medical environment, it must be borne in mind that there will be a wide range of behaviours exhibited. The population within will be fluid and any training will soon be forgotten. The behaviour of patients and visitors will mainly be uncontrolled. Therefore, fire escape routes need to be simple, direct and clearly marked, leading to a designated and suitable safe area; this is normally achieved through a safe zoning compartment system. Infection and security issues will have to be addressed from the start as an integral part of the design.
In the event of fire, babies and non-ambulatory mothers will need to be safely evacuated and there needs to be a detailed strategy for this.	The strategy needs to address issues such as security which may compromise the response and where the mothers and babies can be rapidly accommodated in a warm safe environment, as well as addressing any urgent medical issues.	
Stealing of babies will be a security issue.	Provision of security must not compromise fire escape.	
Increasingly, the fight against infection is central to the choice of materials and their cleaning regimes.	The use of inherently germ-resistant materials with good slip resistance should be considered (eg lino).	
In the UK, the Department of Health has detailed guidance which must be followed.	All relevant advice must be seen at the start of the design process.	

Sources of advice:
- ❑ *Department of Health - Health Technical Memoranda HTMs)*
- ❑ *CIBSE – Hospitals and health care buildings*
- ❑ *DFES Fire safety risk assessment – healthcare premises*
- ❑ *HSE Manual handling in the health service*

NOTES

A prison cell block

FEATURES	THEIR IMPLICATIONS	DISCUSSION
Prisoners are locked in their cells.	Need to release prisoners in case of fire etc OR make cells "safe havens" capable of surviving events.	A prison cell is obviously a hazardous environment where as far as possible hazards need to be designed out and the level of risk reduced.
Movement generally is hampered by security measures.	Can electrical systems be relied upon? Is there manual over-ride?	
The environment is heavily managed at all times.	Unlike most places of work, incidents should be seen and responded to rapidly at all times.	Conversely, the presence of trained staff, normally in control of the environment, enables many hazardous situations to be rapidly responded to and managed through.
Response measures can be planned and staff can be trained and practice response activity.	Unlike most places of work, response to incidents is a major part of the job for all staff.	The unpredictability and potential disruptive behaviour of the prisoners however makes the situation more difficult.
Prisoners may cause or contribute to generally hazardous situations.	Unlike most places of work, there are large numbers of people present with time on their hands who are often inclined to cause or at least join in mayhem.	The management of prisons is a highly skilled activity which includes the provision to prisoners of a reliable, disciplined environment including earned rewards and respect. These contribute to management of the ever-present risks.
Prisoners may attack staff or other prisoners under cover of incidents.		
Prisoners may self-harm or commit suicide.	Some prisoners may present a risk of irrational action which is a hazard to themselves or others.	

Sources of advice: *The Prison Service of the Home Office*

NOTES

A stretch of rural motorway

FEATURES	THEIR IMPLICATIONS	DISCUSSION
Motorways are a workplace for maintenance staff, traffic police and those providing breakdown assistance.		Where decisions are driven by the client, then the client is a designer and responsible for the decision. In the case of highways, where the details of provision are set out in great detail, if a designer wishes to make a change after assessing the in-use risks and the client refuses, it is the clients decision as a designer.
The government strives constantly for safer roads and requirements for safe work during maintenance are laid down by the Highways Agency.		
It is known that stopping on the hard shoulder is hazardous.	Designers should assess ideas such as: (a) whether the provision of periodic off-road lay-byes for repairs is reasonably practicable and (b) whether the provision of rumble-strips at the edge of the hard shoulder would be effective.	Many of the issues arising require a holistic approach with whole-life cost modelling to achieve sensible outcomes.
It is known that working on live motorways – even with good controls – is hazardous.	Design to minimise the need for maintenance should be the aim eg the use of stainless-steel lamp-posts.	

Sources of advice:
- ❑ Designing for maintenance *and other Highways Agency publications*
- ❑ Well-lit Highways *UK Lighting Board, The Stationary Office*
- ❑ *HSE Reducing at-work road traffic incidents*
- ❑ *The risks on motorways have been studied by BRAKE, a charity*

NOTES

A school for infants

FEATURES	THEIR IMPLICATIONS	DISCUSSION
Clearly the main feature is the fact that young children need to be looked after.	Children must be separated form hazards SFARP eg no ponds, controlled access onto roads, good security.	All aspects of the design of a school need to take account of the limitations of children, their possible behaviour and their security and safety.
A school is a specialist environment; whereas general designers may feel they understand it, they are unlikely to.	Designers of schools need to liaise with education experts concerning the real hazards experienced by children.	Both overall layout and the design of means of access from one space to another must be carefully considered to avoid hazards and minimise risk.
Children may behave in an excitable manner	Doors may be slammed trapping fingers in hinges. Children may rush out onto roads to meet their parents, so control of gates is vital. Children are liable to have frequent falls.	The planning of external areas is also important as it will involve vehicle movements and security issues. Issues which are special to children need to be considered (eg hinge protection, safe planting, rounded corners to walls and steps).
Young children may be curious and yet have little understanding of danger.	Access by children to places where they may become trapped or be exposed to hazards (such as hot pipes, ovens, refridgerators etc) must be designed to be controllable. Likewise, plants which are poisonous to humans should not be present.	Issues which apply to both adults and children need to be considered so that the needs of both are taken into account (eg heights of handles, floor finishes).
Security of children is a major concern of all parents and teachers	Prevention of unauthorised access to children must be provided.	
Teachers will wish to mount displays in the classroom and other spaces	Suitable display systems may be designed, eg pulley-operated to avoid standing on desks etc.	
Parents will wish to deliver and collect their children by car	If on-site, provision of a special fenced area is required.	
Teachers will wish to park on-site	Separation of teachers vehicles from children is required.	

Sources of advice:
- ❏ *DFeS Education have a series of Building Bulletins on a wide range of subjects – anyone designing a school must be familiar with them (eg BB85:* School grounds: a guide to good practice *(and) BB87:* Guidelines for environmental design in schools *and many more).*
- ❏ *DFES* Fire safety assessment: educational premises

NOTES

A food processing plant

FEATURES	THEIR IMPLICATIONS	DISCUSSION
Factories are a specialist workplace and employ a range of staff from shift workers, engineers, fitters, electricians, packers, drivers and office staff.	Design of production process is specialized and can be industrially sensitive.	Design should be undertaken in close consultation with the client / end user to ensure the appropriate consideration is given to ERIC process.
Tasks range widely and involve all manner of hazards in the course of the day to day operation. However, many staff generally repeat similar actions or tasks. There can be a high turn over of staff and labour can be unskilled.	Factories constitute a high risk environment particularly to those unfamiliar with the facility	Productivity is a prime driver and training and or controls can be abused to maximize throughput – where possible the design should prohibit abuse of plant or control systems. Consideration is required to the ergonomics in design
Cleanliness and control of contamination. NOTE: Up to 80% of all accidents in food processing plants are slips mainly by poor flooring choice, poor cleaning, gross contamination, poor footwear and condensation. Conditions are often aggressive to products, particularly services and finishes.	The use of suitable finishes and grades of material is essential. Lifespan of finishes need to be considered and maintenance considerations designed in. Once in operation access can be impossible until plant is de-commissioned.	All areas of the production facility should be accessible for cleaning or inspection, hollow sections, voids etc should be designed out. There should be no pathway for foreign matter into the process. Windows and doors should prevent either ingress or support to flaura / fauna. Where not essential glass and timber should be designed out Specified materials must be durable and the lifespan required identified Clients input into performance requirements ideally required.
The layout of plant is driven by the process sequence and operation. The surrounding environment is dependant upon the nature of the process. This can require abnormally high or low temperature etc.	Production areas are frequently congested and confusing. The environment can be unpleasant and or disorientating with particular reference to excessive heat, cold, noise, steam and or aroma	Access for inspection, operation or maintenance including valves etc must be considered within the initial design. Fire escape routes must be clearly defined and maintained The likely environment and its affect on materials (shrinkage, expansion, condensation etc) needs to be known
Hazardous chemicals Moving machinery	High risk to those unfamiliar with environment	Access to particular plant areas / process should be controllable.

Sources of advice:
- ❏ *DFES Fire safety risk assessment – factories and warehouses*

NOTES

Appendices

APPENDIX A – HAZARD CHECKLIST

Introduction

This example is for a small shelter for taxi-drivers to be located alongside a busy street. Inside the shelter there will be facilities for making tea and coffee and hot snacks. The example records the consideration of hazards and risks by the design team at their first design team meeting, which the CDM coordinator attends. He uses the checklist to record the important points discussed and decisions made.

HAZARD	HAZARD ELIMINATION AND RISK REDUCTION

Physical environment
❑ lighting
❑ noise
❑ vibration
❑ temperature
❑ wetness and humidity
❑ draughts.
 	
Chemical/biological environment
❑ sanitary conditions
❑ animals
❑ moulds and fungal growths
❑ hazardous materials
   (solids/liquids/gases/fumes)
❑ smoke
❑ dusts and fibres
❑ contamination/pollution.
 	
Hazardous systems
❑ electricity
❑ hot water and steam
❑ piped gases/liquids
❑ hot/cold surfaces
❑ storage.
 	
Normal activities
❑ posture and manual handling
❑ use of vehicles
❑ use of plant and equipment
❑ industrial processes
❑ use of doors and windows/glazing
❑ use of lifts, escalators and moving
   walkways.
 	
Slips and Trips
❑ while in motion on floors and ramps
❑ while using stairs or escalators
❑ whilst essentially static.
 	
Working at Height
❑ using ladders etc
❑ at unprotected edges/fragile surfaces.
 	
Abnormal events
❑ fire
❑ explosion
❑ falling objects
❑ disproportionate collapse
❑ drowning and asphyxiation
❑ crowding
❑ malicious human intervention.
 	
Anything else?	

APPENDIX B – EXAMPLE OF THE USE OF A HAZARD CHECKLIST TO RECORD TEAM DISCUSSIONS

HAZARD	HAZARD ELIMINATION AND RISK REDUCTION	ACTIONS
Physical environment	The shelter will comply with Building Regulations and will be able to accommodate up to 20 people in a small space. There will be a lobby where wet clothes can be left to dry. The shelter will be maintained as a warm dry space 24/7.	
Chemical/biological environment	Users will eat in the shelter and may or may not use the toilet.	Provide handwash facility at entrance/exit as well as in toilet.
Hazardous systems	Shelter may be left empty for long periods.	All heating (space, water) will be by electricity (no bottled gas). Food heated by microwave oven.
Normal activities	The shelter will comply with Building Regulations.	Chemical toilet to be in a separate naturally-ventilated space.
Slips and trips	Wet shoes and leaves etc.	Flooring must be low-slip-risk material.
Working at height	Single-storey roof to be sloped and self-cleaning finish.	
Abnormal events	Overhanging trees may shed branches.	Suggest LA to be asked to check trees annually.
	Risk of smokers starting a fire.	*Investigate the best way to manage this risk – see notes below.*
	Risk of impact from traffic.	A heavy-duty kerb and guard-rail will be provided.
	Sited in a busy well-lit area. However, there is some risk of fires being started.	Structure to be fire resistant.
Anything else?	Nothing else identified.	

NOTES

Risk of smokers starting a fire was identified as a serious issue. However, after discussion it was considered most unlikely that this would be a safety issue unless

(a)   materials used were highly flammable such that the fire could develop and release toxic fumes before escape was possible or

(b)   there was no-one present, in which case there would only be loss of property. The design team decided to specify fire-resistant materials and to provide a fire extinguisher. Also, after consultation with users, smoking inside the shelter was banned.

APPENDIX C – SOURCES OF FURTHER INFORMATION

NOTES:

1. Wherever possible, references are included in Chapter 3 tables. This appendix contains a list of relevant legislation together with references of a more general nature.

2. Where reference is made to an 'ACoP' this refers to an 'Approved Code of Practice' in support of particular legislation. Some ACoPs contain guidance material. which has a different legal significance.

LEGISLATION and Approved Codes of Practice (ACoPs)

Regulation	How it helps
The **Building Regulations**: currently comprising the following Parts: Part A — Structure Part B — Fire safety Part C — Site preparation and resistance to moisture Part D — Toxic substances Part E — Resistance to the passage of sound Part F — Ventilation Part G — Hygiene Part H — Drainage and waste disposal Part J — Combustion appliances and fuel storage systems Part K — Protection from falling and impact Part L — Fuel conservation Part M — Access to and use of buildings Part N — Glazing safety Part P — Electrical safety – dwellings.	The regulations were conceived primarily for housing standards. The Regulations set out the requirements: each part has its own Approved Documents setting out approved methods for dealing with the requirements and it is these documents which are normally referred to.
The Health & Safety at Work etc Act 1974.	The "head" regulation requiring that workplaces are to be regulated and setting out responsibilities.
The Construction (Design and Management) Regulations 2007 and ACoP 144.	"CDM2007" which drives this guidance.
The Workplace (Health Safety and Welfare) Regulations 1992 – "The Workplace Regulations" and ACoP L24.	Sets out specific requirements for workplaces. (See section 2 above for a summary).
The Management of Health and Safety at Work Regulations 1999 and ACoP L21.	Sets the requirements for those who manage a workplace.
The Disability Discrimination Act 1995 (DDA).	Places obligations on building owners, employers and others to ensure that they do not discriminate against people with disabilities.
The Provision and Use of Work Equipment Regulations 1992 and ACoPs as follows: L22 Safe use of work equipment. L112 Safe use of power presses. L114 Safe use of woodworking machinery.	Known as "PUWER".
Safe use of work equipment. Lifting Operations and Lifting Equipment Regulations 1998 and ACoP L113.	Known as "LOLER".
The Personal Protective Equipment at Work Regulations 1992 and ACoP L25.	Regulations for PPE to be used in a workplace.
The Health and Safety (Display Screen Equipment) Regulations 1992 as amended 2002 and ACoP L26.	Regulations for the use of computers in a workplace.
The Manual Handling Regulations 1992 as amended 2002 and guidance L23.	Regulations for manual handling.
The Control of Substances Hazardous to Health Regulations 2002 and ACoP L5.	Known as "COSHH".

LEGISLATION and Approved Codes of Practice (ACoPs) - cont.

Regulation	How it helps
The Chemical (Hazard Information and Packaging for Supply) Regulations 2002.	Known as "CHIPS" and requiring that suppliers make available data sheets setting out the hazards of materials and products.
The Control of Asbestos Regulations 2006 and ACoP L143.	Regulations for dealing with asbestos.
The Control and Use of Lead at Work Regulations 2002 and ACoP L132.	Regulations for dealing with lead.
The Ionising Radiation Regulations 1999 and ACoP L121.	Regulations for dealing with radioactive materials.
Legionnaire's disease: the control of legionella bacteria in water systems – Guidance L8.	Advises how to manage the risks of Legionnaire's Disease.
Electricity at Work Regulations 1989.	Regulations for electricity.
Gas Safety(Installation and Use) gulations 1998 and ACoP L56.	Regulations for gas.
Dangerous Substances and Explosive Atmospheres Regulations 2002 and a set of ACoPs as follows: L133 – Unloading petrol from road tankers L134 – Design of plant, equipment and workplaces L135 – Storage of dangerous substances L136 – Control and mitigation measures L137 – Safe maintenance, repair and cleaning procedures L138 – Dangerous substances and explosive atmospheres.	Regulations and guidance for dangerous substances and explosive atmospheres.
The Control of major accident hazards regulations 1999.	Known as "COMAH".
Safety of pressure systems. Pressure Safety Systems Regulations 2000 and ACoP L122.	Regulations for pressure systems.
Safe Work in Confined Spaces Regulations 1997 and ACoP L101.	Regulations for work in confined spaces.
The Regulatory Reform (Fire Safety) order 2005.	Relates to fire assessment of the workplace.
The Work at Height Regulations 2005.	Regulations for working "at height"
The Control of Vibration at Work Regulations 2005 and ACoPs as follows: L140 Hand-arm vibration. L141 Whole-body vibration.	Regulations for vibrations which affect people.
The Control of Noise at Work Regulations 2005.	Regulations for noises which affect people
Health and Safety (Consultation with Employees) Regulations 1996 and Guide L95.	Requires consultation with non-unionised employees.
The Health and Safety (Safety Signs and Signals) Regulations 1996 and ACoP L64.	Regulations for safety signs etc.
REGULATIONS APPLICABLE TO SPECIFIC INDUSTRIES	
Container terminals: Safe working practice HSG7.	Container terminals.
Docks Regulations 1988 and ACoP COP25.	Docks.
Control of Substances Hazardous to Health in the Production of Potteries, ACoP L60.	Potteries.
Shipbuilding and Ship Repairing Regulations 1960.	Shipbuilding and repair.

HSE Guidance

Note thatfurther guidance is available through the HSE website, including downloadable simple guides; search on topic words as listed there.

Guidance	How it helps
Five steps to risk assessment INDG163	Explains the basics of risk assessment.
Essentials of health and safety at work HSE Books.	Explores the subject of occupational health.
Planning for health and safety when selecting and using catering equipment and workplaces. Catering Info sheet 9.	Advice particular to catering facilities.

Other reference material

Guidance	How it helps
BS8300:2001 Design of buildings and their approaches to meet the needs of disabled people.	A code of practice to assist detailed design.
BS8437:2005 Code of practice for selection, use and maintenance of personal fall protection systems and equipment for use in the workplace.	A code of practice for personal fall protection systems.
BSRIA Rules of Thumb (BG14/2003).	Sets out typical requirements for different spaces and suggests allowances to make at scheme design stage.
CIBSE guides: ❑ Volume A Environmental design ❑ Volume B Heating, ventilation, air conditioning and refrigeration ❑ Volume D Transportation systems in buildings ❑ Volume E Fire engineering ❑ Volume G Public health engineering ❑ Volume K Electricity.	These design guides provide design information and calculation techniques. They are continually under review and update.
CIRIA C605, *Operating and maintenance manuals for buildings, a guide to procurement and preparation.*	Guidance on O+M manuals.
CIRIA C581, *Facilities management manuals – a best practice guide.*	Guidance on FM manuals.
HSE Catering Information Sheets.	A series of sheets giving advice on issues in the catering world, covering the key inherent risks.
HSE Health and safety in engineering workshops HSG129.	Guidance for engineering workshops.
BRE: Building regulation, health and safety, BR417.	Analysis of in-use H+S risks, including discussion of medical conditions.
Reports from SCOSS (Standing committee on structural safety).	Advice about issues of concern reported by professionals.

Websites

www.citb-constructionskills.co.uk/CDM	Industry guidance
www.hse.gov.uk	The HSE website – see the Construction Industry area
www.hsebooks.co.uk	Search for publications
www.safetyindesign.org	Industry guidance
www.dbp.org.uk	Case studies
www.scoss.org.uk	SCOSS website

CIRIA C663

London 2007

CDM2007 – Workplace "in-use" guidance for designers

A Gilbertson

CIRIA *sharing knowledge* ∎ *building best practice*

Classic House, 174–180 Old Street, London EC1V 9BP
TELEPHONE 020 7549 3300   FAX 020 7253 0523
EMAIL enquiries@ciria.org
WEBSITE www.ciria.org

Summary

The Construction (Design and Management) Regulations 2007 (CDM2007) apply to construction work undertaken in the UK and for all projects for which designers will have duties under CDM. This guide helps any person or organisation acting as a designer to meet their obligations with respect to designing, taking account of *workplace 'in-use' hazards*. (Advice on considering *construction* hazards is provided in CIRIA Publication C662, *CDM2007 – Construction work sector guidance for designers*, which also contains more general information about designers' duties under CDM).

The legal duty under CDM to consider workplace "in-use" hazards is explained, and advice is given on how it may be effectively discharged, taking account of the Approved Code of Practice (ACoP) publication L144. In addition to giving advice on a designer's legal duties, the guide explains how the work may be carried out in an effective, proportionate manner. The issue of "who is a designer for the purposes of CDM" is addressed.

CDM2007 – Workplace – "in use" guidance for designers

Gilbertson, A

CIRIA publication C663   © CIRIA 2007   ISBN: 978-0-86017-663-3
                                                    0-86017-663-0

British Library Cataloguing in Publication Data
A catalogue record is available for this book from the British Library.

Keywords		
Health and safety, construction management, Construction (Design and Management) Regulations, CDM, CDM2007, construction work, demolition, design, designers, hazards, maintenance, risk, workplace		
Reader Interest	**Classification**	
Construction industry designers, architects, civil engineers, structural engineers, services engineers, surveyors, consultants, local authorities, facility managers	AVAILABILITY CONTENT STATUS USERS	Unrestricted Original research Committee guided Construction sector designers, (engineers, architects, surveyors, project managers), CDM coordinators Construction industry professionals

Published by CIRIA, Classic House, 174-180 Old Street, London EC1V 9BP.